Grammar Rules!

High-Interest Activities for Practice and Mastery of Basic Grammar Skills

Book 3

by Jillayne Prince Wallaker

Dedication

With lots of love to Maegen, Madalen, Ian and always to Willie.

Credits

Editors:
Tracy Soles, Donna Walkush

Layout Design:
Victory Productions, Inc.

Illustrations:
Janet Armbrust

Cover Design:
Peggy Jackson

First South Asian Edition, 2006
- 4262/3, Ansari Road, Daryaganj, New Delhi 110 002, E-mail: vivadelhi@viviagroupindia.net
- 215-216 New Apollo Estate, 2nd Floor, Mogra Lane, Andheri (E), Mumbai 400 069 E-mail: vivamumbai@viviagroupindia.net
- Jamal Fazal Chambers, 26 Greams Road, Chennai 600 006, E-mail: vivachennai@viviagroupindia.net
- B-103, Jindal Towers, 21/1A/3 Darga Road, Kolkata 700 017, E-mail: vivakolkata@viviagroupindia.net
- 7 Sovereign Park Appts., 56-58, K.R. Road, Basavanagudi, Bangalore 560 004 E-mail: vivabangalore@viviagroupindia.net
- 101-102 Moghal Marc Apartments, 3-4-637 to 641 First Floor, Narayanguda, Hyderabad 500 029 E-mail: vivahyderabad@viviagroupindia.net

Published in arrangement with

Published by Vinod Vasishtha for Viva Books Private Limited, 4262/3, Ansari Road, Daryaganj, New Delhi 110 002.

Printed and bound at Raj Press, R-3, Inderpuri, New Delhi-110 012

ISBN 81-309-0014-9

Contents

Contents

Introduction

Grammar Rules! was developed so that writing teachers can show students that grammar can be understood (and sometimes even fun) when presented in a clear, reasonable way. *Grammar Rules!* builds on each topic in a logical progression so that students learn the facts behind the skill, practise the skill, then are able to put their new grammar knowledge into action.

After each grammar skill is introduced, plenty of practice is provided, along with a Review Work and a Draft Book exercise for students to transfer their new skill. Review Work assignments focus on previously covered skills or provides additional practice with a skill on the given page. The Draft Book assignments encourage students to apply the grammar skills and incorporate them into their own writing. For the Draft Book activities, students can complete assignments on loose-leaf paper in a folder or in a spiral or composition notebook.

Each grammar skill presented in the Review Work and Draft Book exercises has a locator code, such as underlining nouns with yellow. This code is consistent throughout the series. This provides a student with a patterned tool for self-monitoring as well as self-editing.

This book also contains a comprehensive review on pages 112-114. These pages are perfect for a pre- and post-assessment or an end-of-year test.

A student editing checklist is included on page 115. This page is designed to be used as a self-editing tool. By assigning two or three items to check at a time, students are not overwhelmed with "getting everything right," but instead can focus on very specific skills until they understand them completely. Once mastery of the selected editing skills is evident, an additional set of items can be assigned. The same piece of student writing can be used for several editing assignments or students can use different writing samples. This convenient checklist can be kept with student Draft Books as a reminder of grammatical variations that can be included in their writing. It can also be used to monitor student progress by dating each skill when it is demonstrated consistently.

Grammar Rules! will quickly become a resource that writing teachers return to for strong grammar activities to show their students that grammar really does rule!

Name ______________________

Rocks

parts of speech

The main parts of speech include the following: nouns, verbs, pronouns, adjectives, adverbs and conjunctions.

Write the part of speech for each numbered word on the line.

(1)Arun studies rocks and minerals with his class. The class observes rocks, performs field tests on the minerals and reads extensively about both. He discovered that there are three (2)types of rocks: sedimentary, igneous and metamorphic.

Sedimentary rocks are formed in layers. The layers are deposited in streams and riverbeds. Sand, pebbles, plant matter and (3)animal parts can all end up in these layers. Over time, the layers (4)solidify, and sedimentary rock is formed. The (5)plant matter and animal parts become fossils.

Igneous rocks are formed in, under and around volcanoes. The molten rock, or heated liquid rock, forms underground. (6)It is called magma. Some magma cools (7)slowly underground, becoming igneous rock. Pressure causes other magma to rise to the surface. When magma (8)exits the volcano, its name changes to lava. Lava flows from the volcano, incinerating everything it touches. (9)Finally, it cools. (10)Solidified lava is igneous rock. Igneous rocks have many different looks depending on how (11)quickly they cool. Igneous rock can have air bubbles and be very light, (12)or it can be jet black and very solid.

Metamorphic rock is changed rock. It (13)forms deep underground. Sedimentary or igneous rock that has been compressed by underground pressure (14)and heat becomes metamorphic rock. The heat and pressure cause the layers of sedimentary and igneous rock to become meshed together, much like the cheese in a grilled-cheese sandwich meshes (15)slightly with the bread on each side.

(16)These three rock types are the literal (17)building blocks of Earth. (18)They provide stability to our structures and provide many building materials for the items (19)we use daily. Arun finds rocks (20)fascinating.

1. ______________
2. ______________
3. ______________
4. ______________
5. ______________
6. ______________
7. ______________
8. ______________
9. ______________
10. ______________
11. ______________
12. ______________
13. ______________
14. ______________
15. ______________
16. ______________
17. ______________
18. ______________
19. ______________
20. ______________

Review Work

Underline 10 nouns in this piece of writing with yellow.

Draft Book

Locate a piece of your writing. Underline nouns with yellow. Underline verbs with blue.

Name ______________________________

Categories

nouns

Nouns are words that name people, places, things or ideas.

Underline the nouns in the sentences. Write each noun in the correct category below.

Narendra vacations on an island in the Andamans.

Kangaroos live in Australia.

The crowd clapped and cheered.

Karuna studied flowering plant pollen.

Those sweaters belong to Mahima.

Sabu, Nizam and Miss Priya went to the tennis courts.

The bird in that cage belongs to Koel.

Their family went to Colombo.

The rabbit left tracks in the snow in our yard.

The cafeteria in our school is great.

People: ______________________________

____

Places: ______________________________

____

Things: ______________________________

____

Review Work

Draw an X next to each proper noun that names a person. Draw a triangle above each proper noun that names a place.

Draft Book

Make lists of people you know, places you have been and things that interest you. Write 10 nouns for each list. Use these nouns in future writing assignments.

Name ______________________________

They Are Special

common and proper nouns

Proper nouns name specific people, places, things or ideas. A person's first and last names are proper nouns, as well as titles like Mr., Mrs., Miss, Dr., etc. A proper noun always begins with an uppercase letter. All other nouns are common nouns. A common noun does not begin with an uppercase letter.

For each proper noun, cross out the lowercase letter and write the uppercase letter above it. Put an uppercase letter at the beginning of each sentence.

frédéric auguste bartholdi, a frenchman, designed the statue of liberty.

the gateway of india is in mumbai, maharashtra.

hussain sagar lake separates hyderabad and secunderabad.

in delhi, you can see the red fort and visit raj ghat.

konark in orissa is famous for the sun temple.

mahesh, tinku and arun are trekking in ladakh.

Write a proper noun for each common noun.

People

teacher: ____________________ student: ____________________

adult: ____________________ doctor: ____________________

Places

state: ____________________ restaurant: ____________________

school: ____________________ continent: ____________________

Things

toy: ____________________ food: ____________________

animal: ____________________ book: ____________________

Review Work

Underline the names of people in the sentences with yellow.

Draft Book

Write five sentences using proper nouns.
Underline each noun with yellow. Capitalise the proper nouns.

Name ______________________________

He, She or It

gender nouns

Gender is the sex referred to by a noun. The English language has four genders: masculine (male), feminine (female), neuter (no sex) and indefinite (either sex).

Circle the indefinite nouns.

classmates	niece	team	ducks	mare	student	nephew	siblings
mail carrier	people	aunt	relatives	queen	animals	parents	prince
champion	friend	milk	player	book	singer	umbrella	pencil

Write the underlined nouns in the proper categories. Add two of your own nouns to each category.

A knight in shining armour saved the princess from the dragon.

My grandmother is a doctor, and my uncle is a nurse.

Our cousins have roosters and hens in a coop.

The king wanted the jester to do tricks and sing songs.

Her sister and brother roasted hot dogs and marshmallows.

Masculine: ______________________________

Feminine: ______________________________

Neuter: ______________________________

Indefinite: ______________________________

Review Work

Draw an X above each noun in the sentences that names a person.

Draft Book

Write two sentences for each noun category. Above each noun, indicate the gender: M = masculine, F = feminine, N = neuter or I = indefinite.

Name ______________________________

I'll Take These Plural

plural nouns

A plural noun is a noun that names more than one person, place, thing or idea.

Usually, add an *s* to make a noun plural: cat + s = cats
If a singular noun ends in *ch*, *s*, *z*, *sh* or *x*, add es: patch + es = patches
If a noun ends in *f* or *fe*, change *f* or *fe* to *v* and add es: life + es = lives
If a noun ends in a consonant + *y*, change the *y* to *i* and add es:
party + es = parties
If a noun ends in a vowel + *y* or a vowel + o, add *s*: boy + s = boys
If a noun ends in a consonant + o, add es: tomato + es = tomatoes

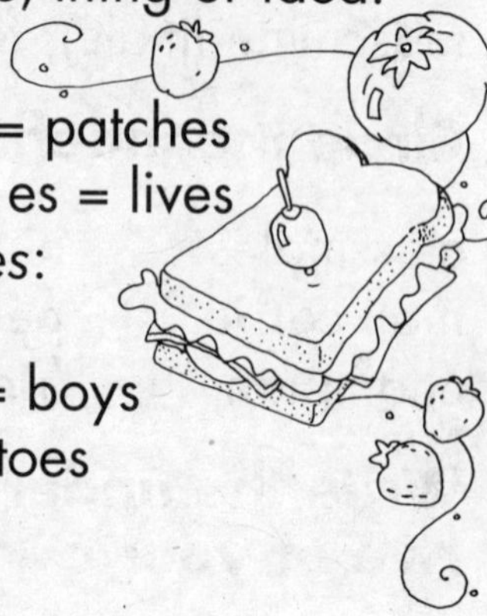

Write the plural form of each singular noun.

stereo	____________	sandwich	____________
buzz	____________	crash	____________
match	____________	ax	____________
wife	____________	calf	____________
thief	____________	radio	____________
elf	____________	lady	____________
country	____________	city	____________
guppy	____________	jelly	____________
hobby	____________	strawberry	____________
pass	____________	chimney	____________
boy	____________	toy	____________
bay	____________	turkey	____________
domino	____________	potato	____________
hero	____________	video	____________

Review Work

Draw a star next to each person and place noun.

Draft Book

Choose 10 noun pairs (singular and plural forms). Write a sentence for each noun.

Name ______________________________

Tricky Nouns — irregular plural nouns

Some nouns change in the middles or ends when they become plural. Others do not change when they become plural.

examples (change): axis → axes medium → media
examples (no change): bison, deer, moose, series, sheep, swine

Match the singular and plural nouns. Write the number in front of the singular noun in the box in front of the correct plural noun.

1. goose	☐ phenomena
2. phenomenon	☐ teeth
3. hippopotamus	☐ children
4. mouse	☐ feet
5. tooth	☐ people
6. cactus	☐ men
7. child	☐ cacti
8. foot	☐ geese
9. person	☐ oxen
10. louse	☐ octopuses
11. octopus	☐ dice
12. man	☐ hippopotamuses
13. woman	☐ lice
14. die	☐ women
15. ox	☐ mice

Review Work

Write the plural form of the following nouns:

flower __________ crisis __________ pitcher __________ life __________

Draft Book

Write a story using some of the tricky nouns on this page. Circle the plural nouns. Draw a star next to each singular noun.

Name ______________________________

Mine, All Mine

possessive nouns

A possessive noun shows belonging. If a noun is singular or if it is plural but does not end with an s, add an apostrophe + s to the end to make it possessive.

example: cat's food, boss's pen, men's belts

If a noun is plural and already ends with an s, add an apostrophe to the end.

example: cats' collars, dancers' shoes

Change the following ownership phrases into phrases using possessive nouns.

the toys belonging to the brothers ______________________

the brush belonging to Ifaat ______________________

the ball belonging to the twins ______________________

the bike belonging to his sister ______________________

the pencil belonging to Mrs. Ali ______________________

the pillow belonging to Adam ______________________

the score book belonging to the team ______________________

Circle each possessive noun. Write *SP* if it is singular possessive or *PP* if it is plural possessive.

__________ The dog's new, leather collar is lost.

__________ The snails' aquarium needed cleaning.

__________ The art project's colours were faded by the sun.

__________ We peeked into the teachers' lounge.

__________ Pramod borrowed Sachi's new crayons.

__________ The dancers' audience clapped wildly.

__________ The children's balloons blew away.

Review Work

Underline the plural nouns with yellow.

Draft Book

Write 10 sentences using possessive nouns. Include both singular possessive and plural possessive nouns.

Name ____________________________________

Action

action verbs

An action verb is a word that tells what someone or something is doing.

example: The boy **swims** at the beach.

Circle each verb.

A jar of fireflies provides nearly enough light to read by.

Scientists used a spectrometer to learn more about solar light.

Fluffy scrambled eggs melt in your mouth.

Tarun filled the colander with apples.

Silkworms spin cocoons of silk thread.

Water condenses on icy glasses in the summer.

Rita tumbled down the sand dune.

Sandeep and I designed a cultural outfit.

George swings the golf club.

The cat claws the furniture.

Nita calculates the total.

Butterflies flutter from one flower to another.

Daya shivers without her coat and hat.

The table-tennis ball bounced across the table.

Sai and Mohit played football.

Review Work

Write an N above each neuter noun.

Draft Book

Find a page of writing in your Draft Book with the nouns underlined with yellow.Underline the verbs with blue.

Name ______________________________

Lunch in the Inlet

action verbs

An action verb is a word that tells what someone or something is doing.

Fill in the blanks with verbs from the list or choose your own. Use each word only once.

appears	captures	cruises	devours	glides
gulps	scouts	shines	sift	slides
slips	snags	snaps	teems	sits

The inlet ______________________ calm and quiet.

Below, the murky water ______________________ with life.

A crayfish ______________________ at a passing minnow.

The minnow ______________________ small water organisms.

A pike ______________________ its territory.

His meal ______________________ right across his path.

Ducks ______________________ along the surface of the water.

Duck bills ______________________ through the mud looking for treats.

A little, green frog ______________________ on a lily pad.

The frog ______________________ a fly buzzing just out of reach.

A snake ______________________ into the water eyeing the unwary frog.

The snake ______________________ the frog.

A turtle ______________________ off a log.

The sun ______________________ down beginning a lazy afternoon.

Review Work

Write an *I* above each indefinite pronoun.

Draft Book

Find a page of your writing in your Draft Book or write a story about what happens in the cafeteria during lunch. Underline the nouns with yellow and the verbs with blue.

Name ______________________________

Action

action verbs

An action verb is a word that tells what someone or something is doing.

example: The boy **swims** at the beach.

Circle each verb.

A jar of fireflies provides nearly enough light to read by.

Scientists used a spectrometer to learn more about solar light.

Fluffy scrambled eggs melt in your mouth.

Tarun filled the colander with apples.

Silkworms spin cocoons of silk thread.

Water condenses on icy glasses in the summer.

Rita tumbled down the sand dune.

Sandeep and I designed a cultural outfit.

George swings the golf club.

The cat claws the furniture.

Nita calculates the total.

Butterflies flutter from one flower to another.

Daya shivers without her coat and hat.

The table-tennis ball bounced across the table.

Sai and Mohit played football.

Review Work

Write an N above each neuter noun.

Draft Book

Find a page of writing in your Draft Book with the nouns underlined with yellow.Underline the verbs with blue.

Name ____________________________

Lunch in the Inlet

action verbs

An action verb is a word that tells what someone or something is doing.

Fill in the blanks with verbs from the list or choose your own. Use each word only once.

appears	captures	cruises	devours	glides
gulps	scouts	shines	sift	slides
slips	snags	snaps	teems	sits

The inlet ____________________ calm and quiet.

Below, the murky water ____________________ with life.

A crayfish ____________________ at a passing minnow.

The minnow ____________________ small water organisms.

A pike ____________________ its territory.

His meal ____________________ right across his path.

Ducks ____________________ along the surface of the water.

Duck bills ____________________ through the mud looking for treats.

A little, green frog ____________________ on a lily pad.

The frog ____________________ a fly buzzing just out of reach.

A snake ____________________ into the water eyeing the unwary frog.

The snake ____________________ the frog.

A turtle ____________________ off a log.

The sun ____________________ down beginning a lazy afternoon.

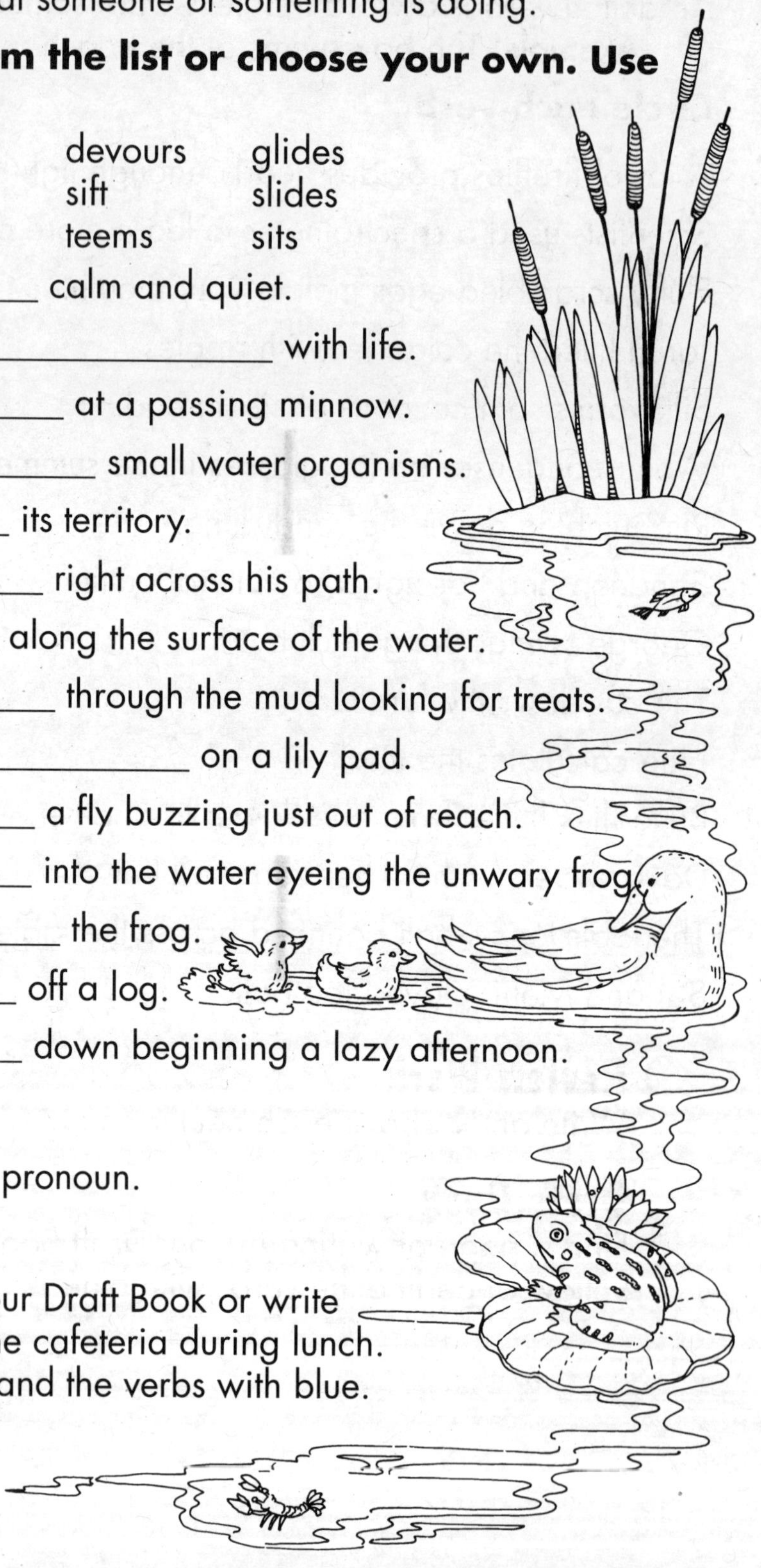

Review Work

Write an *I* above each indefinite pronoun.

Draft Book

Find a page of your writing in your Draft Book or write a story about what happens in the cafeteria during lunch. Underline the nouns with yellow and the verbs with blue.

Name ______________________________

Give a Helping Hand

helping verbs/ verb phrases

Helping verbs are verbs that help main verbs express tense. There are 23 helping verbs. A verb phrase acts as a single verb and is made of a main verb with one or more helping verbs. Up to three helping verbs can precede the main verb. *Would*, *should*, *shall* and *will* are helping verbs. Forms of the following verbs are also helping verbs:

be: am, are, is, was, were, be, being, been
do: do, does, did
have: have, has, had
may: may, must, might
can: can, could

Circle the helping verbs. Underline the verb phrases.

The fleas did jump through the cat's fur.

The water is pouring into the basement.

The ant had scurried into the anthill.

We are going to the amusement park.

I am excited to be here.

The lights can be dimmed with this switch.

Mudit was entitled to his turn.

The puppy must have tried to jump onto the bed.

That jam would make a good ice-cream topping.

The bird had flown into the bushes.

We should weed the garden before it gets too hot.

The tickets may cost too much.

Sabeena's family might go to the zoo tomorrow.

Review Work

Underline the nouns with yellow.

Draft Book

Write 10 sentences that use helping verbs. Circle the helping verbs. Underline the verb phrases with blue.

Name ______________________________

Link Them Together linking verbs

A linking verb is a verb that does not show action. It links or joins something in the predicate to the rest of the sentence. It does not have an action verb after it. Forms of the verb *to be* are the most common linking verbs. There are eight forms of the verb *to be*: *am, are, is, was, were, (will) be, (am, are, was, were) being, (have, has, had) been*. Other linking verbs include forms of these verbs: *to appear, to become, to feel, to grow, to look, to remain, to seem, to smell, to sound* and *to taste*.

Underline the linking verbs.

The knitted sweaters are very warm.

The food on the table appears appetising.

The neighbour's dog, who was sprayed by a skunk, smells awful.

The garbage can by the door is full.

That frozen drink tastes fruity.

The lilac bushes, planted when I was born, grow more beautiful every year.

Lata, Apu's big sister, is our junior counsellor.

Anush, my younger cousin, will be in first grade next year.

The moon was like a huge orange ball hovering in the sky.

The music, which played for hours, grew increasingly louder.

Ms. Tania, my mom's friend, is a pediatric neurosurgeon.

Mom's new scissors are sharp enough to cut corrugated cardboard.

Mr. Suresh, my orthodontist, is nice.

Last night Venus was visible low in the sky.

Review Work

Draw a star above each person noun.

Draft Book

Write 10 sentences that use linking verbs. Use a variety of the linking verbs listed above. Underline the linking verbs with blue.

Name ______________________________

Choose the Verb

noun and verb agreement

A singular noun uses a verb with an *s* at the end. A plural noun uses a verb that does not have an *s* at the end.

examples: The **boy climbs** the tree.
The **boys climb** the tree.

A verb uses the same rules as a noun when adding *s* or *es*.

Usually, add an *s* to a verb: run + s = runs
If a verb ends in *sh*, *s*, *z*, *ch* or *x*, add *es*: pitch + es = pitches
If a verb ends in a consonant + *y*, change *y* to *i* and add *es*: try - y + i + es = tries
If a verb ends in a vowel + *y*, add *s*: enjoy + s = enjoys

Circle the correct verbs.

Neha (stare, stares) at the massive mess in her room.

Jay and I (catch, catches) outfield balls.

Students (choose, chooses) which vegetables to eat.

Numerous plants (thrive, thrives) in the rain forest.

People (access, accesses) the Internet.

Not many minnows (survive, survives) to become adult fish.

Debu (complain, complains) about mowing the lawn.

Squirrels (flee, flees) when my sister opens the sliding door.

Santosh (invite, invites) his friends to a sleepover.

Soumi and Swati (agree, agrees) on the answer.

Our kites (fly, flies) through the air at the beach.

Mother (half, halves) the candy bar for us to share.

Tara (spread, spreads) jelly onto the peanut butter sandwich.

Review Work

Draw an X above each proper noun in the sentences that names a person.

Draft Book

Choose five of the sentences. Rewrite each one so that the first noun is the opposite (singular or plural) of what it is now. Rewrite the verb to agree with the new subject.

Name ____________________________

Subjects

simple subject of a sentence

The simple subject of a sentence is the noun that the sentence is about.

example: Preet's **fish** swam in the aquarium.
example: Mount Everest is the tallest mountain in the world.

Underline the noun that is the simple subject of each sentence.

Most tree branches grow at an acute angle from the tree trunk.

The rupee rolled under the cabinet.

Chandu's watch was slow by an hour.

The thermometer read 62 degrees Fahrenheit.

The Marianas Trench is deeper than Mount Everest is tall.

Mount Rushmore towers over the valley.

The praying mantis is related to the cockroach.

My mom made homemade pineapple jam.

Ladybugs assist farmers by eating harmful insects.

Garnet is the January birthstone.

Abhijit vacationed in Kolkata.

Parrots require lots of attention.

Bamboo is not a tree.

Paul teased Talia about the food in her lunch.

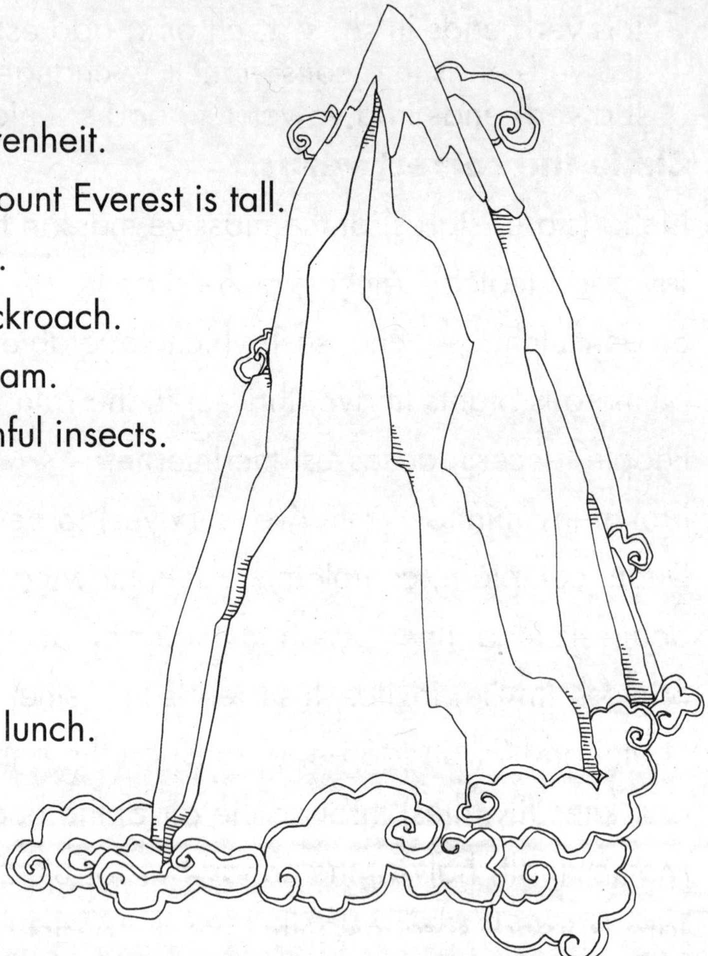

Review Work

Circle the plural nouns.

Draft Book

Find a full page of writing in your Draft Book or write a story about your favourite hobby or sport. Write an *SS* above the simple subject in each sentence.

Name ________________________________

Fill in the Subject

simple subject of a sentence

The simple subject of a sentence is the noun that the sentence is about.

example: Anna's **bike** is red.

example: Mount Rushmore required years of effort to construct.

Add a simple subject to each sentence by using a singular or plural noun as indicated. If a proper noun is used, capitalise it.

singular A ________________________ can be used for drawing.

singular ________________________ is an ingredient of this meal.

plural Many ________________________ grow on trees.

singular The little ________________________ crawled across the picnic table.

plural ________________________ can destroy homes.

plural Gopi's remote-controlled ________________________ are awesome.

singular The ________________________ hovered over the red flower.

plural ________________________ are great places to visit.

singular The ________________________ is in the backyard.

plural The ________________________ disagree about everything.

singular A large ________________________ works well for this task.

plural ________________________ eat only plants.

singular ________________________ is my favourite park.

plural ________________________ are great to read.

singular An ________________________ is a healthy snack.

plural Those ________________________ should be washed.

Review Work

Underline the nouns that are not simple subjects with yellow.

Draft Book

Find a full page of writing in your Draft Book. Write an SS above the simple subject in each sentence.

Name ______________________________

Pick the Pronoun subject pronouns

A pronoun takes the place of a noun. Subject pronouns take the place of simple subject nouns. They are *I*, *you*, *he*, *she*, *we*, *they* and *it*.

Above each set of nouns, write the pronoun that could take each word's place. Add four nouns to each list.

____

peninsula ______________
monorail ______________
dog ______________
television ______________

____

Aunt Maya ______________
Sarla ______________
Mrs. Shenoy ______________
Mother ______________

____

the choir ______________
Monu and Ram ______________
the team ______________
the customers ______________

____

George and I ______________
my brother and I ______________
my class and I ______________
you and I ______________

____

Mr. Mittal ______________
the king ______________
Uncle Mohan ______________
Binoy ______________

Replace the words in bold type with subject pronouns. Write the correct pronoun on each line.

Venu removed the fender and repaired it. ______________

The moon is full and bright tonight. ______________

Gowri and I invented a new sandwich. ______________

Dogs raided our garbage can. ______________

Mrs. Bansal gave us a pop quiz today. ______________

Review Work

Underline the nouns in the sentences above with yellow.

Draft Book

Find a page of writing in your Draft Book. Change the subject nouns to subject pronouns.

Name ____________________________________

Doing What?

simple predicate

The simple predicate is the main verb of the sentence that tells what someone or something is doing.

Underline each simple predicate.

Suraj panicked when he noticed his lunch money missing.

The stars shimmered across the night sky.

Monarch caterpillars devour milkweed leaves.

Mosquitoes transmit malaria.

Chitra grabbed the swing with both hands.

The monkey turned around.

Ritik took his fifth wicket in a row.

The roller coaster catapulted its riders forward.

Tears poured from their eyes.

Annie and Sarah gathered the blankets.

Dhanesh completed the order form.

He soaked them with the hose.

Mr. Shetty answered their questions.

Manohar and I counted the money.

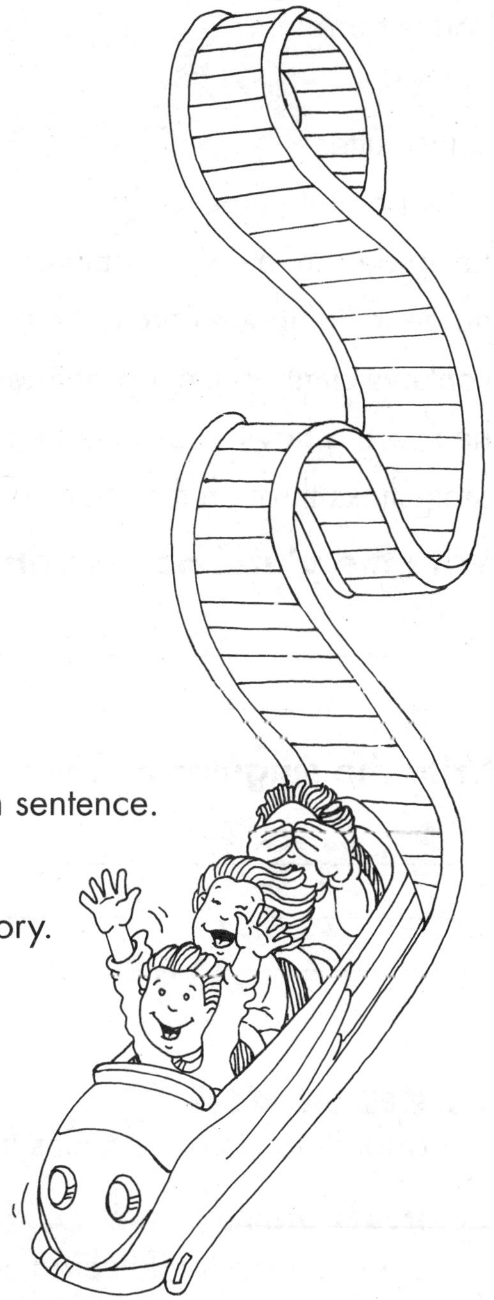

Review Work

Write an *SS* above the simple subject in each sentence.

Draft Book

Use one of the sentences on this page in a story.
Underline the simple predicates with blue.

Name ________________________________

The Animal World

simple subjects and predicates

The simple subject of a sentence is the noun that the sentence is about. The simple predicate is the verb that tells what someone or something is doing.

Underline each simple subject once. Underline each simple predicate twice.

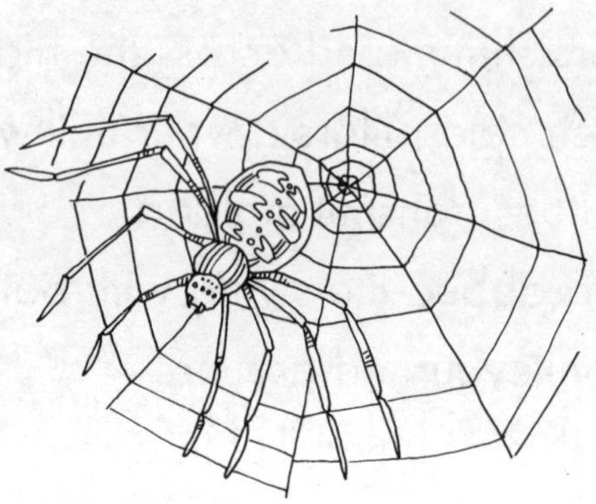

An owl watches.

Worms burrow.

A dolphin surfaces.

Moths flutter.

An elephant trumpets.

The spider on the web captures an unwary fly.

The deer stampede across the plains.

Monkeys climb to the top of trees to eat fruits.

The soaring hawk scans the land for small rodents.

A fox slinks through the underbrush towards the rabbit.

Write the plural nouns with their verbs.

________________________ ________________________

________________________ ________________________

Write the singular nouns with their verbs.

________________________ ________________________

________________________ ________________________

________________________ ________________________

Review Work

Underline the other nouns in the sentences with yellow.

Draft Book

Begin a verb list. Record interesting verbs for use in future writing assignments.

Name ______________________________

It Happened Before

past tense

Tense tells time. It informs the reader when the sentence takes place. If the action happened in the past, it is past tense. There are several ways to make a verb past tense.

Usually, add *ed* or *d* to a verb: box + ed = boxed, wave + d = waved.

If a verb ends with a consonant + *y*, change *y* to *i* and add *ed*: carry - y + i + ed = carried.

If a verb has a short vowel with one consonant, double the consonant then add *ed*: tip + p + ed = tipped, stop + p + ed = stopped.

Use the rules above to make the verbs past tense.

rustle	______________	end	______________
bat	______________	cry	______________
splatter	______________	trip	______________
agree	______________	snap	______________
ship	______________	create	______________

Write the correct past tense verb on each line.

Satish (copy) ______________ his work onto clean paper.

The kitten (pounce) ______________ on the ladybug.

Smrti (try) ______________ spinach for the first time.

The firefighter (parachute) ______________ into the fire zone.

Raju (hurry) ______________ to his piano lesson.

Aparna (play) ______________ with her cousin.

Zuhoor (shop) ______________ for new shoes.

Review Work

Write an *SS* above the simple subject in each sentence.

Draft Book

Choose five verb pairs (present and past tense). Write two sentences for each verb. Use the present tense verb in one sentence and the past tense verb in the other.

Name ________________________________

Now or Then

past and present tense

Tense tells time. When it happened in the past, it is past tense. When something happens now, it is present tense.

Underline the verb in each first sentence. Write the past tense of the verb in each second sentence.

Children crawl through the obstacle course.

Yesterday, they ______________________ through by the hundreds.

Mosquitoes bother the horses.

They ______________________ the dogs last week.

Collin bounces on the trampoline.

He ______________________ on it with Anand earlier.

Chitra and I roll the chapati dough very carefully.

We ______________________ enough dough to make six dozen chapatis.

The doctor inoculates the child.

She ______________________ several children this morning.

Tara and Nilesh drift along on the inner tubes.

They ______________________ downstream.

The news helicopter hovers over the scene.

It ______________________ there until the photos were taken.

Mahesh tastes the broccoli salad.

He ______________________ the chutney earlier.

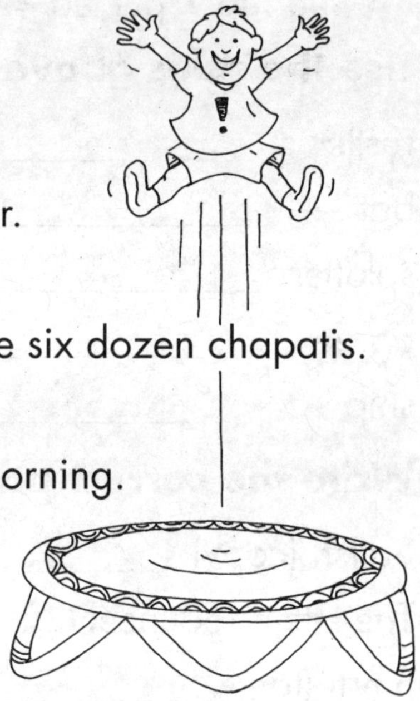

Review Work

Underline the subject nouns in the first sentences with yellow. Underline the pronouns that replaced them in the second sentences with red.

Draft Book

Find a story you wrote in your Draft Book. Put boxes around verbs with *ed* endings.

Name ______________________________

Now and Then

past and present tense

Tense tells time. It informs the reader when the sentence takes place. One way to make a verb past tense is to add *ed* to the end.

past tense: Sam **studied** for the test.
present tense: Sam **studies** for the test.

An irregular verb becomes past tense by changing its spelling.

example: catch/caught, shine/shone, sting/stung

Circle the simple predicate. Identify the tense of the verb by writing *past* or *present* on the line.

Bees buzz around the daisies. ____________________

Madhu brushes sand from her legs. ____________________

Priya ate ice cream. ____________________

The parakeet nibbled on crackers. ____________________

Kareena bandages the cut on her knee. ____________________

Kapil sharpened his pencils for the test. ____________________

Kris disturbs the teacher. ____________________

Raj and Jamil left the theatre. ____________________

The hamsters race around their cages. ____________________

Anand wrote a great acrostic poem. ____________________

Sally photographs our field trips. ____________________

My brother taught me to tie my shoes. ____________________

Venu shovels sand into the sandbox. ____________________

Jeena threw hay into the horse stalls. ____________________

Dilip cried for his bottle. ____________________

Review Work

Write an *SS* above each simple subject.

Draft Book

Write five sentences using present tense verbs and five sentences using past tense verbs.

Name ________________________________

Things to Come

future tense

Tense tells time. It informs the reader when the sentence takes place. To make a verb future tense, add the helping verb *will* before the singular present tense form of the verb. If the verb has an ending, drop it before adding *will*.

example: Babu **rakes** the lawn. Babu **will rake** the lawn.
Jan **ate** the apple. Jan **will eat** the apple.

Write the correct future tense verb on each line.

Jairam (builds) ______________________ a birdhouse.

Ali (caught) ______________________ some fish.

The boat (cruises) ______________________ around the channel.

Balu and Raghu (jumped) ______________________ into the pool.

The class (observes) ______________________ the plants as they grow.

Jay (painted) ______________________ that set of chairs.

The monkey (grabbed) ______________________ the rope.

Kunal (helped) ______________________ make the cake.

Charu (completed) ______________________ the book.

A dolphin (bumps) ______________________ the boat gently.

Jyoti (brought) ______________________ cupcakes for the party.

The sauce (burns) ______________________ with the burner on high.

Diya (carries) ______________________ the pineapples to the car.

Ayan, Manoj and Jacob (threw) ______________________ water balloons.

The silverware (clatters) ______________________ to the floor.

Review Work

Underline the nouns with yellow.

Draft Book

Write about an imaginary trip using future tense verbs.

Name ______________________________

Past, Present or Future

verb tenses

Verbs use tenses to tell when something is happening.

Underline the verbs. If a verb is future tense, underline both the main verb and the helping verb *will*. Circle past, present or future.

The barrel collects rainwater.	past	present	future
Jamie writes to her friend.	past	present	future
Leena will microwave the popcorn.	past	present	future
Jackie planted the garden.	past	present	future
Murukesh will arrange the flowers.	past	present	future
The soup boiled over onto the stove.	past	present	future
Kaushik will lounge in the hammock.	past	present	future
The saw cut through the tree limb.	past	present	future
The driver backed into the parking space.	past	present	future
Heena slapped the card onto the table.	past	present	future
The chef prepares dinner.	past	present	future
The jellyfish will float on the waves.	past	present	future
Rema pesters her sister.	past	present	future
Niraj will bait the hook.	past	present	future
Nilesh will chew the strawberry bubble gum.	past	present	future
Madhu and Deb manipulate the controls.	past	present	future
Richa searched for frogs and crayfish in the pond.	past	present	future

Review Work

Underline the nouns with yellow.

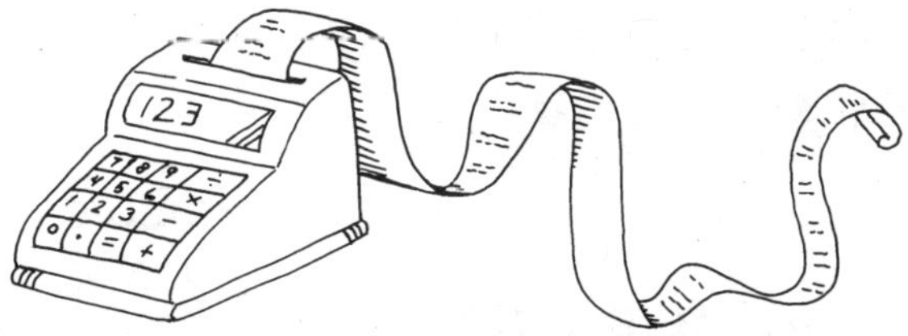

Draft Book

Write two sentences for each verb tense.
Underline the verbs with blue. Label the sentences past, present or future tense.

Name ______________________________

Regular Describers

adjectives

Adjectives are words that describe nouns. Adjectives tell what kind, how many or which one. They can include number, colour, size, shape, or other detail words.

examples: The **dirty** puppy needs a bath. The **public** library is closed today.

A sentence can have more than one adjective.

example: **Four grey** bugs are in the **small** garden.

Circle the adjectives. Draw an arrow from each adjective to the noun it describes.

A wood-handled shovel leaned against the old, red wheelbarrow.

The filthy refrigerator needed to be scoured.

I have mint gum in my top drawer.

The new purple pen is leaking ink.

Five colourful birds swooped through the warm air.

A tired Babu found muddy footprints on the clean floor.

A riderless skateboard zoomed down the steep hill.

Alisha jumped into the cool pool water.

The itchy bumps were not bug bites.

The glowing coals were ready to cook the raw hamburger.

Grandma gave us cherry pie with vanilla ice cream.

An uncooperative child threw an enormous fit in the restaurant.

Review Work

Underline the simple predicates twice.

Draft Book

Write 10 sentences that have adjectives in them. Circle each adjective. Draw an arrow from the adjective to the noun it describes.

Name ____________________

Other Describers

demonstrative and common adjectives

Adjectives are words that describe nouns. Adjectives tell what kind, how many or which one. They can include number, colour, size, shape or other detail words. The four demonstrative adjectives that answer which one are: *this*, *that*, *these* and *those*. Common adjectives are regular adjectives.

Circle the adjectives. Draw an arrow from each adjective to the noun it describes.

Those scented candles produce very hot wax.

That four-year-old child chatters constantly.

This fuzzy peach has a bruised spot.

Those majestic glaciers tower above this cruise ship.

That dirty blue sock has a small hole in the toe.

This yellow pencil has a broken point.

My little sister is in that class.

Vineet wants that chocolate cupcake with white frosting.

Veena drew that seaside sketch with the thunderous storm clouds.

These tiny black seeds can grow delicious white radishes.

Those glass marbles belong to that boy.

That black camera takes great photographs.

Review Work

Write a *D* above each demonstrative adjective.

Draft Book

Write 10 sentences that have adjectives in them. Circle each adjective. Draw an arrow from the adjective to the noun it describes.

Name ______________________________

Special Describers

proper adjectives

Adjectives are words that describe nouns. The four demonstrative adjectives are: *this*, *that*, *these* and *those*. Common adjectives are regular adjectives. Proper adjectives are made from proper nouns. They are always capitalised. However, the nouns they modify are usually not capitalised. Some proper adjectives are spelt the same as the proper nouns.

example: Mom has **Coorg** oranges and **Kashmiri** apples on that shelf.

Other proper adjectives have different spellings than the proper nouns.

example:	noun: Switzerland	adjective: Swiss
	noun: China	adjective: Chinese

Underline the nouns. Circle the proper adjectives.

The luxury car's seats were made of Italian leather.

Rahul ordered Hyderabadi biryani and Kerala shrimp.

William Shakespeare is a famous English playwright.

Koel wore her Japanese kimono for the festival.

Did you see the Chinese dragon on the menu cover?

Nissim's family observes the Jewish tradition of lighting the menorah.

The Bangalore roads were lined with trees.

Sydney is a coastal Australian city.

Many unusual creatures live in Brazilian rain forests.

The Egyptian exhibit at the museum was filled with interesting artefacts.

Review Work

Draw an arrow from each proper adjective to the noun it describes.

Draft Book

Write 10 sentences that have adjectives in them. Include proper, demonstrative and common adjectives. Circle each adjective and draw an arrow to the noun it describes.

Name ____________________

Choose Your Adjective

adjectives

Adjectives are words that describe nouns. The four demonstrative adjectives are: *this*, *that*, *these* and *those*. Common adjectives, like common nouns, are not capitalised. Proper adjectives are made from proper nouns. They are always capitalised. However, the nouns they modify are not usually capitalised.

Underline the nouns. Circle the proper adjectives. Draw an arrow from each proper adjective to the noun it describes.

That Agra petha is absolutely delicious.

Sunita studied about Roman emperors for her social studies test.

The Arctic region is home to little, white, baby harp seals.

Abu made an acute angle on that triangle.

We are eating Gujarati food for dinner tonight.

Those noisy birds woke up the entire neighbourhood.

Neena went to a Chennai zoo to see the cute Nilgiri Tahrs.

Sohan parked his green mountain bike next to that chain-link fence.

The best hunters around are the Bengal tigers.

My grandmother has Hyderabadi pearls in her jewel case.

My Pakistani relatives hosted an Iftar party this year.

Review Work

Write a *D* above each demonstrative adjective.

Draft Book

Write 10 sentences that have adjectives in them. Include proper, demonstrative and common adjectives. Circle each adjective. Draw an arrow from the adjective to the noun it describes.

Name ______________________________

At the End

adjectives: positive, comparative, superlative

Adjectives describe and/or compare nouns. There are three degrees of comparison. The positive degree describes a noun (or nouns). The comparative degree compares two nouns (add *er* or the words *more* or *less*). The superlative degree compares more than two nouns (add *est* or the words *most* or *least*).

Usually, comparative and superlative adjectives are formed by adding the suffixes *er* and *est* with no changes to the base words. There are some exceptions.

If an adjective ends with e, drop the e and add *er* or *est*: rare + est = rarest.

If an adjective ends in a consonant + *y*, change *y* to *i* and add *er* or *est*: funny - y + er = funnier.

If an adjective has a short vowel with one consonant, double the consonant then add *er* or *est*: mad + d + er = madder.

If an adjective has two or more syllables, use *more*, *most*, *less* or *least* in front of it.

Add *er* and *est* to each adjective to make the comparative and superlative forms.

Positive	Comparative	Superlative
angry	____________	____________
wise	____________	____________
fast	____________	____________
great	____________	____________

Add *more* and *most* to each adjective to make the comparative and superlative forms.

Positive	Comparative	Superlative
delicious	____________	____________
interesting	____________	____________
vibrant	____________	____________
majestic	____________	____________

Review Work

Write the comparative and superlative forms of the following adjectives: lucky, delightful, tame, sad, old.

Draft Book

Write 10 sentences using comparative and superlative forms of adjectives.

Name ______________________________

-Er or More

adjectives: positive, comparative, superlative

Usually, comparative and superlative adjectives are formed by adding *er* and *est*, but for a few adjectives, the spelling must be changed. Comparative and superlative adjectives can also be formed by adding the comparison words *more*, *most*, *less* or *least*. However, when using the comparative and superlative forms of an adjective do not precede the adjective with these words.

example: Divya is smarter. (yes)
Divya is more smarter. (no)
Divya is most smarter. (no)

Circle the correct adjectives.

The (nearest, more nearest) restaurant is four miles away.

This hot chocolate is (hotter, most hot) than I like it.

My friend Preeti is the (most nicer, nicest) person I know.

That movie is (more interesting, interestinger) than the one we watched last week.

This book is (less intenser, less intense) than its sequel.

This assignment is (harder, more harder) than yesterday's was.

The (best, more best) hot dogs are those toasted on an open fire.

My parents are the (least happy, least happier) when I get home late.

That batch of laddus is (sweeter, more sweeter) than this batch.

Your head is (more protecteder, more protected) with a bike helmet.

We tasted the (more worst, worst) lunch in history today.

The (most gigantic, most giganticest) spider ever just crawled across the floor.

The (older, more older) basketball is the (more better, better) ball.

Review Work

Write an *SS* above the simple subject in each sentence.

Draft Book

Write 10 sentences using comparative and superlative forms of adjectives.

Name ______________________________

Odd Adjectives

present and past participles

A participle is a verb form. It acts as an adjective. The present participle is the *ing* form of a verb. The past participle usually ends in *d* or *ed*.

examples: The **crying** baby was hungry. The **tired** child was crabby.

present participle *past participle*

Circle each present or past participle. Draw an arrow to the noun it modifies. Write *pres* for present participle or *past* for past participle.

________ Sajia's favourite book is the battered one on the middle shelf.

________ You must stay away from the whirling power saw blade.

________ We avoided the broken glass in the parking garage.

________ The enraged hornet flew after the horse.

________ Kamal prefers to avoid the spinning rides.

________ Totu, the parakeet, always bothers the napping puppy.

________ The thawed desserts are in the refrigerator.

________ Babu will blow out the burning candles.

________ Jaleel could not open the tightly closed jar.

________ Sunit washed the serving bowl and put it away.

________ The reading area was full, so Sam read at his desk.

________ Madhu put her muddied shoes on the deck.

Review Work

Underline the simple subjects once and the simple predicates twice.

Draft Book

Write 10 sentences that use present and past participles. Draw an arrow from each participle to the noun it modifies.

Name ____________________________________

They're Confused

irregular verbs and participles

Usually, a regular verb forms the past tense and past participle by adding *d* or *ed* to the present tense verb. An irregular verb forms the past tense and past participle by changing spelling and can end with *t*, *en* or *n*.

examples: bite → bitten — The robber was bitten by the police dog.
freeze → frozen — The frozen yogurt was delicious.

Circle the correct verbs and participles.

The mother blue jay has (sitted, sat) on her eggs for many days.

Her (shrinked, shrunk) shirt was never worn again.

The towering, old pine had (fell, fallen) during the snowstorm.

Abhay will have (spoked, spoken) on the phone for two hours.

The girls had (swinged, swung) on the tyre swing before us.

Rohan and Preet have (swimmed, swum) in the river before.

The nanny goat at the zoo had (ate, eaten) the lace off my sock.

Tarun had (setted, set) his camera on the picnic table.

The carefully (maked, made) birthday cake was beautiful.

The fishermen had (arosed, arisen) before the sun came up.

Surabhi has (catched, caught) several monarch butterflies in her net.

That nasty hornet had (stinged, stung) Sasha's hand.

Seema and Shan have (slided, slid) down the snowy hill on their sled.

The (broke, broken) vase lay in pieces on the floor.

Review Work

Circle the plural nouns.

Draft Book

Write 10 sentences using irregular verbs. Underline the verbs with blue. Underline the nouns with yellow.

Name ______________________________

Just to Be Perfect
perfect tenses

The three perfect verb tenses indicate completed action. They are formed using the past participle (usually verb + *d* or *ed*) and the helping verbs *had*, *has* or *(will) have*.

past perfect: She **had known** the answer.
present perfect: She **has known** the answer.
future perfect: She **will have known** the answer.

Circle each past participle and its helping verb(s). Write *SP* for past perfect, *PP* for present perfect, or *FP* for future perfect on the line.

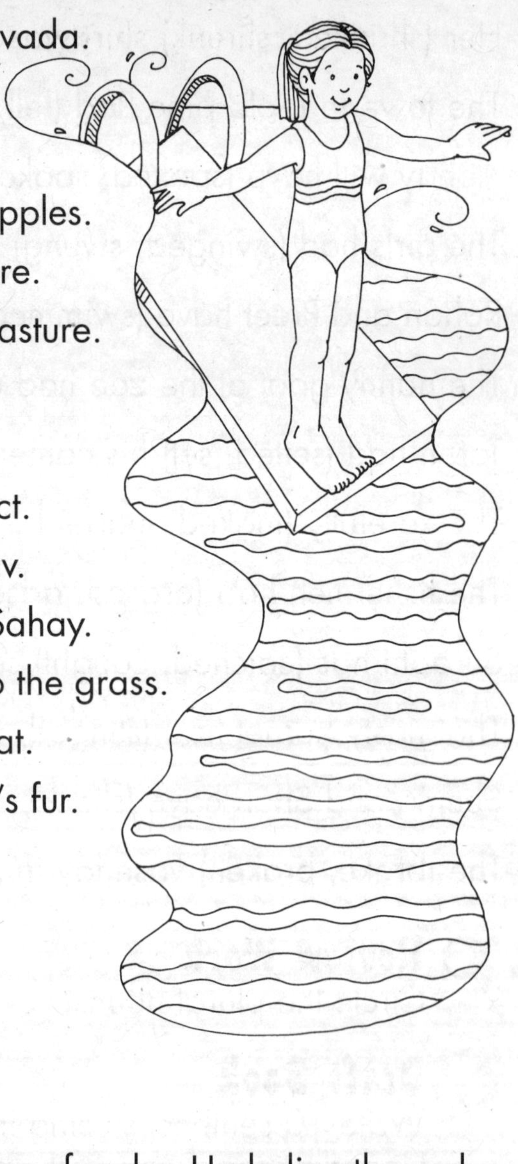

_________ Brinda has burnt her tongue on that hot vada.
_________ Lakshmi will have done her work.
_________ Tara will have dived off the high dive.
_________ Abhay and Tara have bitten into their apples.
_________ Laxman will have biked to the video store.
_________ The sheep will have gone to the back pasture.
_________ Kamla's cat has caught a mouse.
_________ The quarter has fallen into the drain.
_________ Anita had worked on her science project.
_________ Pran had travelled to Ajmer with Gaurav.
_________ Devi and Kris will have spoken to Ms. Sahay.
_________ The small green snake has slithered into the grass.
_________ Anil has asked for a large root beer float.
_________ The baby koala had clung to its mother's fur.
_________ Nikita had taken her craft set home.
_________ The sun had shone all week long.

Review Work
Underline the complete subjects once.

Draft Book
Write 10 sentences using the perfect tense forms of verbs. Underline the verbs with blue.

Name ______________________________

Ongoing Action

progressive tense

The progressive verb tense indicates action in progress. It uses the present participle (verb + *ing*) and a form of the helping verb *to be*. Present progressive tense uses *am, is* and *are*. Past progressive tense uses *was* and *were*. Future progressive tense uses *will be*.

Circle each progressive verb and its helping verb(s). Write *SPg* for past, *PPg* for present or *FPg* for future on the line.

_______________ The pot of spaghetti noodles was boiling for seven minutes.

_______________ The crickets will be chirping all night long.

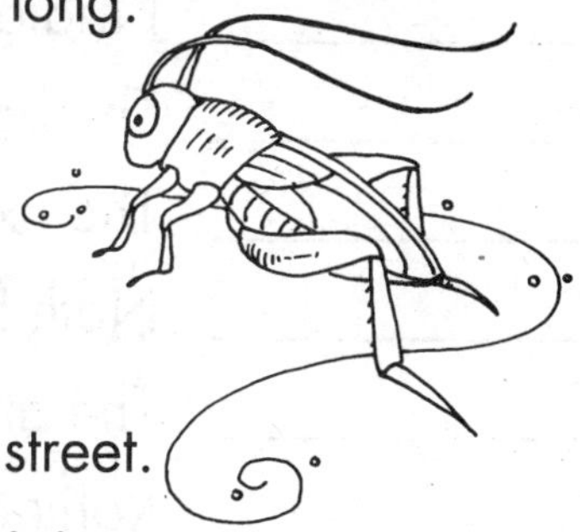

_______________ Sajeev is sneezing.

_______________ Abu was coughing all night.

_______________ Mala is swinging in the backyard.

_______________ The ice-cream truck is coming up the street.

_______________ The children will be swimming at the lake.

_______________ The rabbits were playing hide-and-seek with the children.

_______________ My sister Leena is knitting a sweater for my birthday.

_______________ Jairam is working on the computer.

_______________ Jameela was drinking a chocolate-milk shake.

_______________ Suman is biking to Jalil's house.

_______________ Grandma Seeta was buying produce at the farmers' market.

_______________ We will be visiting the museum on Tuesday.

_______________ Nikhil is hammering the board into the joist.

Review Work

Circle the plural nouns.

Draft Book

Write 10 sentences using progressive tense verbs. Underline the verbs with blue.

Name ______________________________

How, Where or When — adverbs

Adverbs are words that modify verbs, adjectives or other adverbs. They tell how often, where, when or to what extent something happens. Most adverbs end in *ly*. Three commonly used adverbs are *not*, *very* and *too*.

Circle each adverb. Indicate how it modifies by writing *how, where, when* or *what* on the line.

___________ Geeta quickly finishes her paper.

___________ Atul always reminds us to buckle our seat belts.

___________ Nadia and I ate a large breakfast this morning.

___________ The barking dog was annoyingly loud.

___________ The exhausted children went inside.

___________ Nath frequently drinks milk with his meals.

___________ The athlete gracefully executed the flip.

___________ Rohit plays too much golf.

___________ Brinda silently crept up the stairs.

___________ Rohini and Malar read often.

___________ Lisa chatters incessantly.

___________ Dad drove backward into the garage.

___________ Vineet played the music quietly.

___________ Rekha will work on her painting tonight.

___________ The fruit salad is very healthy.

___________ The plan was brilliantly thought out.

___________ The storm wildly pounded the windows.

___________ Devan walks daily with his friend.

Review Work

Circle the adjectives. Draw an arrow from each adjective to the noun it describes.

Draft Book

Write a story about your favourite month of the year. Include adverbs. Circle the adverbs with purple.

Name ______________________________

Good or Well

adjectives/adverbs

Good, *well*, *bad* and *badly* are often confused. *Good* and *bad* are adjectives. *Well* and *badly* are adverbs.

Circle the correct words. Draw an arrow from each adjective to the noun it describes.

The dancers performed the number (good, well).

Rita tried not to choose any (bad, badly) mangoes.

Ankit plans to rent a (good, well) video.

Arun says he fishes (good, well) when he is in the boat.

Harish felt (bad, badly) when his bike was stolen.

Mina did (good, well) on her last maths test.

That story isn't written (bad, badly).

I can't hear (good, well) when the television is so loud.

Aswini is not a (bad, badly) golfer.

Plug your ears because my sister sings (bad, badly).

Uma wants to do a (good, well) job on her sculpture.

They got lost because of the (bad, badly) set of directions.

That book is so (good, well), I would recommend it to anyone.

The chocolate cake with fudge icing is (good, well).

If Sachin hits (bad, badly) in this game, he will probably practise all weekend.

We want a (good, well) cook; the last one was (bad, badly).

The play was (good, well), but the lead actor performed (bad, badly).

Review Work

Draw an X next to each proper noun that names a person.

Draft Book

Write 10 sentences. Include an adjective or adverb from this page in each sentence.

Name ______________________________

Glasses and Sleep

time adverbs

Adverbs modify verbs, adjectives or other adverbs. Time adverbs tell when or how often. Time adverbs include: *before, continuously, early, eventually, finally, first, frequently, immediately, last night, lately, never, nightly, now, often, once, periodically, rarely, sometimes, soon, then, today, tonight, tomorrow* and *usually*.

Write a time adverb on each line. Use words from the list above. Do not use words more than once.

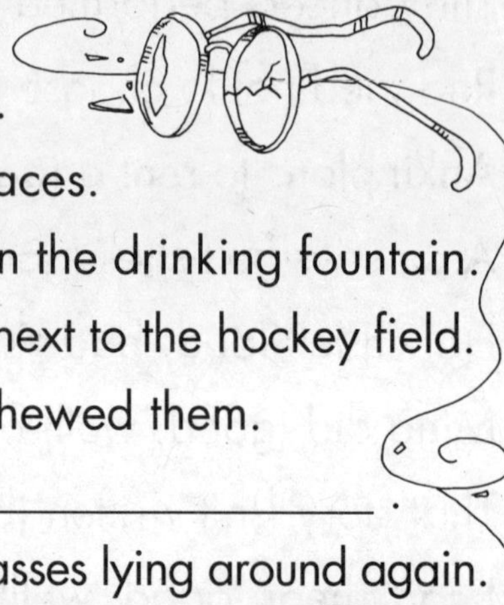

Gautam ______________________ loses his glasses.

They are ______________________ found in odd places.

His glasses were ______________________ found on the drinking fountain.

______________________, he left them on the ground next to the hockey field.

______________________, the dog found them and chewed them.

His mother is taking him to get new glasses ______________________.

Gautam promised ______________________ to leave his glasses lying around again.

Nitya is ______________________ wide awake and attentive.

She is very tired ______________________.

Nitya did not get much sleep ______________________.

Her baby brother cried ______________________.

______________________, she drifted off to sleep.

We hope they both sleep better ______________________.

Choose a time adverb not used in the sentences above. Use it in a sentence of your own.

____

____

Review Work

Underline the subject pronouns with red.

Draft Book

Begin a list of time adverbs to use in future writing assignments. Write 10 sentences with adverbs.

Name ______________________________

Crawly Things

place adverbs

Adverbs can modify verbs, adjectives or other adverbs, but they usually modify verbs. Place adverbs tell where.

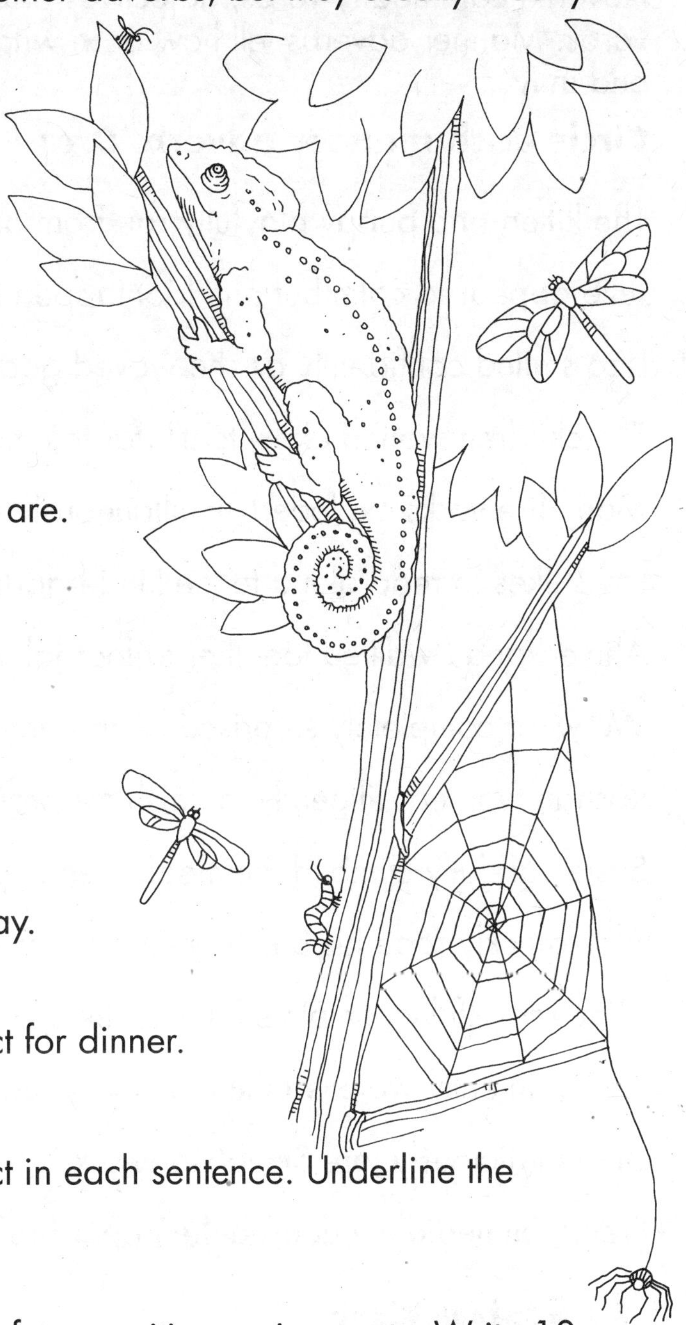

Circle the place adverbs.

Many crawly things live outside.

I like them better there than inside.

They seem to be everywhere you look.

They are below, above and beside.

Ants congregate underground.

Worms live there, too.

Mosquitoes seem to be anywhere people are.

One buzzed close to my ear.

Insects are always nearby.

Dragonflies hover overhead.

That apple has a worm inside.

Bluebirds swoop down to grab insects.

A chameleon looks backward for insects.

Preeti would like it if spiders lived far away.

A spider's web is over there.

A spider dropped down to wrap an insect for dinner.

Review Work

Write an *SS* above the simple subject in each sentence. Underline the verbs with blue.

Draft Book

Begin a list of place adverbs to use in future writing assignments. Write 10 sentences with adverbs.

Name ______________________________

How'd You Do That? manner adverbs

Adverbs can modify verbs, adjectives or other adverbs, but they usually modify verbs. Manner adverbs tell how or in what manner an action is performed. Many end in *ly*.

Circle each manner adverb. Draw an arrow to the verb it modifies.

The kitten and puppy playfully ran from one end of the room to the other.

Julie appeared calm but one foot tapped nervously.

Liza smiled confidently as she waved good-bye to her parents.

The children waited expectantly for the movie to begin.

Many fireworks exploded simultaneously in the night sky.

Louis likes to read aloud to the kindergartners.

Ahmed and I walked together to football practice.

We were completely surprised by the announcement.

Roshan worked diligently to finish his project by Friday.

Susie carefully climbed the maple tree to get the kitten down.

Alok quickly rode his bike home in order to meet his curfew.

Minu regretfully completed the exciting book.

Harish intently watched the ants carry load after load into the anthill.

Uma maliciously tore Smita's artwork.

Prema immediately doused the paper fire with water.

Review Work

Underline the nouns with yellow.

Draft Book

Begin a list of manner adverbs to use in future writing assignments. Write 10 sentences with adverbs.

Name ______________________________

Comparatives

adverbs: positive, comparative, superlative

Adverbs describe and/or compare verbs, adjectives and other adverbs. There are three degrees of comparison. The positive degree describes a verb, adjective or other adverb. The comparative degree compares two actions (add *er* or the words *more* or *less*). The superlative degree compares more than two actions (add *est* or the words *most* or *least*).

If an adverb ends with *ly*, use *more*, *most*, *less* or *least* in front of it: alertly (positive), more alertly (comparative), most alertly (superlative).

Add *er* and *est* to each adverb to make the comparative and superlative forms.

Positive: late, calm, near, soon, early

Comparative: ______________________________

Superlative: ______________________________

Add *more* and *most* to each adverb to make the comparative and superlative forms.

Positive: safely, skilfully, brilliantly, easily

Comparative: ______________________________

Superlative: ______________________________

Circle the comparative and superlative adverbs. Write which form of the adverb is used on each line.

__________ Debu answered more rapidly than Sami.

__________ Rohan woke up the earliest.

__________ Suresh returned home sooner than expected.

__________ I can finish this more quickly if you let me do it myself.

__________ Jaya described the directions the most clearly.

__________ The youngest puppy most eagerly attacked the bone.

Review Work

Underline the simple predicate in each sentence with blue.

Draft Book

Write 10 sentences using comparative and superlative forms of adverbs.

Name ________________________________

Fruits and Veggies

articles: a, an, the

A, *an* and *the* are articles. An article comes before a noun or adjective/noun combination. Use *a* in front of words that start with a consonant sound. Use *an* in front of words that start with a vowel sound. Use *the* if reference is being made to a specific thing or things.

Write *a* or *an* in front of these items.

________ apricot	________ Himachali apple	________ tomato
________ onion	________ papaya	________ orange
________ mango	________ aubergine	________ pineapple
________ apple	________ cabbage	________ avocado
________ honeydew	________ artichoke	________ Empire apple
________ cherry	________ watermelon	________ banana

Write *a, an* or *the* on each line.

I am making ________ salad. Would you help me? Bring me ________ lettuce from ________ refrigerator. Please get ________ spinach and ________ coriander leaf. Cut ________ celery stalk and ________ cucumber into slices. You can slice ________ onion, too. ________ radishes and ________ carrots are in the crisper. ________ fruit salad would be good, also. There is ________ orange, ________ apple and ________ banana on the counter. ________ cherries and ________ grapes are washed and in ________ bowl behind ________ milk. Put ________ sliced watermelon and ________ cubed cantaloupe on a plate. There is ________ honeydew on the shelf. It can be sliced and put on ________ plate.

Review Work

Underline the subject pronouns with red.

Draft Book

Find a story in your Draft Book. Circle the articles with orange. If an article is incorrect, fix it.

Name ________________________________

The Entire Thing — complete subject

The simple subject is the noun that the sentence is about. The complete subject is the simple subject plus any articles or adjectives that describe or modify that noun.

example: The striped ball rolled down the hill.
ball = simple subject
The striped ball = complete subject
article ↗ ↖ *adjective*

Circle the simple subjects. Underline the complete subjects.

An itsy-bitsy bug will crawl under your beach towel.
Those five scary costumes were chosen for the play.
That incredibly high roller coaster causes people to scream.
The earsplitting tornado rampaged through town.
Those sharp knives have protective covers on them.
Our old, battered road atlas helped us determine travel routes.
Those neon-coloured crayons add vibrant details to pictures.
My icy-cold fingers will need a pair of warm gloves.
Minu's little sister played the game all afternoon.
That very long number is not a palindrome.
Kunal's sunburnt shoulders hurt.
Saravan moved to Chennai.
That smelly lotion tingles on my skin.
The luminescent insects flickered on and off in the quiet darkness.

Review Work

Underline the simple predicates with blue. Write the verb tense beside each sentence: S = past, P = present and F = future.

Draft Book

Write 10 sentences. Circle the simple subjects and underline the complete subjects.

Name ______________________________

Get the Rest

complete predicate

The simple predicate is the verb that tells what someone or something is doing. The complete predicate is the simple predicate plus any helping or linking verbs and any adverbs that describe or modify the verb.

example: The marble can roll smoothly.
roll = simple predicate
can roll smoothly = complete predicate

helping verb (→ can) *adverb* (→ smoothly)

Circle the simple predicates. Underline the complete predicates.

The black and brown puppy may have been bought already.

That spotted dog often races around.

A hornet will sting quickly.

Little brown tree frogs buzz continuously.

The colourful parrot squawked most loudly.

The little golden hamster scurries around.

Mourning doves will wake up earliest.

The marble-sized hail suddenly pounded down.

The glowing coals shimmered more brightly.

Dolphins must surface often.

The number four race car accelerated rapidly.

Aamir often works slowly but accurately.

That large stain will need prompt attention.

This disgusting tasting medicine was swallowed very quickly.

Review Work

Indicate the verb tense used in each sentence. Write the verb tense beside each sentence: S = past, P = present and F = future.

Draft Book

Write 10 sentences with helping verbs and adverbs modifying the simple predicates. Underline the complete predicates with blue.

Name ______________________________

The Whole Predicate

complete predicate

The complete predicate is the simple predicate plus any helping or linking verbs, any adverbs, and any other words that modify the verb. If the words are not part of the complete subject, they are included in the complete predicate.

example: Bobby will bike to the beach.

The big, red apple fell to the ground.

Sally played with her brother.

Circle the simple predicates. Underline the complete predicates.

Violet was responsible for feeding the fish.
The glass of soda spilled across the table.
The sun sparkles blindingly off the snow.
The enormous block tower toppled.
Sleepy children awoke to frosted windows.
The winter snowman melted away to nothing.
Manisha slept with one arm around her teddy bear.
The price of stamps will rise at the end of June.
The glowing space heater pumps out waves of comforting heat.
The dinner-plate-sized blooms popped open overnight.
The striped beach ball drifted just out of reach.
Alisha surfaced coughing and sputtering.
This suction cup will stick securely to the window.

Review Work

Indicate the verb tense used in each sentence. Write the verb tense beside each sentence: S = past, P = present and F = future.

Draft Book

Write 10 sentences. Underline the complete predicates with blue.

Name ______________________________

Looking for Sentences

complete sentences

A sentence needs one complete subject and one complete predicate.

example: Jan has a dog. = sentence

complete subject *complete predicate*

a dog = not a sentence

A sentence can be long or short.

example: Jan walks.

complete subject *complete predicate*

The tiny little bird with the broken wing ← *complete subject*
finally flew out the door and into the backyard. ← *complete predicate*

If the group of words is a sentence, put a star in the box. Underline the complete subject once and the complete predicate twice. If the group of words is not a sentence, put an X in the box.

- ☐ Jamila, the girl with black hair
- ☐ is a great talent
- ☐ Akhil took a peek at the bird's nest
- ☐ a quadrilateral is a four-sided shape
- ☐ Hari handed in his assignment
- ☐ Pamela likes to draw
- ☐ a rupee or more
- ☐ goodness, that room is messy
- ☐ have a pet frog
- ☐ you can order a book

Review Work

Add an uppercase letter at the beginning and the correct punctuation mark at the end of each group of words that is a sentence.

Draft Book

Make complete sentences out of the groups of words that are not sentences.

Name ______________________________

Make the Fix

sentence fragments

A sentence needs one complete subject and one complete predicate. A sentence fragment is a group of words missing either the subject or the predicate.

Add a subject or predicate to each sentence fragment to make a complete sentence. Put an uppercase letter at the beginning and the correct punctuation mark at the end.

wandering down the path through the woods

____

Raghu, who arrived from South India,

____

gathered the ingredients

____

the animal in the very last cage

____

the most incredible thing

____

fell asleep on the couch

____

ran across the sand

____

are detailed and accurate

____

stepped on its tail

____

Review Work

Underline the complete subjects once and the complete predicates twice.

Draft Book

Choose one sentence from above and use it in a story.

Name ___________________________

Predicate Nouns

linking verbs and predicate nouns

A linking verb does not show action. It links or joins something in the predicate to the subject of the sentence. It does not have an action verb after it. A predicate noun is a noun that follows the linking verb and tells something about the subject.

Underline the linking verbs. Circle the predicate nouns. Draw an arrow from each predicate noun to the simple subject it tells more about.

Bamboo is a tall, treelike grass.

That girl in the third row was my sister.

Mrs. Sharma is a fifth-grade teacher.

I am a good student.

A solar calculator is a great maths tool.

Jupiter is a massive ball of gas.

Venus is the second planet from the sun.

The first-chair violin player is Matthew Bolan.

Our sun is actually a star.

That lumpy, dark green stone is raw jade.

This little seed will be a great banyan tree someday.

Those ladies are the staff surgeons tonight.

That lady in a red sari appears to be a teacher.

Acrophobia is the fear of heights.

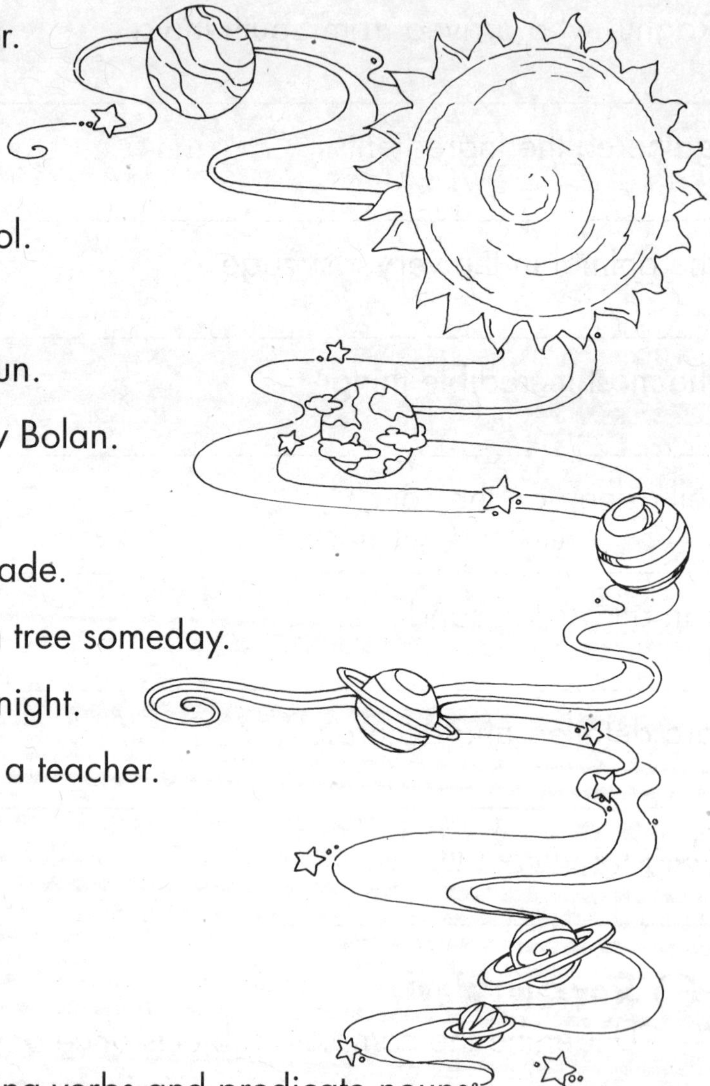

Review Work

Circle the adverbs with purple.

Draft Book

Write 10 sentences that use linking verbs and predicate nouns.
Draw an arrow from each predicate noun to the subject it tells more about.

Name ______________________________

Summertime

linking verbs and predicate adjectives

A linking verb does not show action. It links or joins something in the predicate to the subject of the sentence. It does not have an action verb after it. A predicate adjective is an adjective that follows the linking verb and tells something about the subject.

Underline the linking verbs. Circle the predicate adjectives. Draw an arrow from each predicate adjective to the simple subject it tells more about.

Ants in the house are disgusting.

Juicy hamburgers on the grill are delicious.

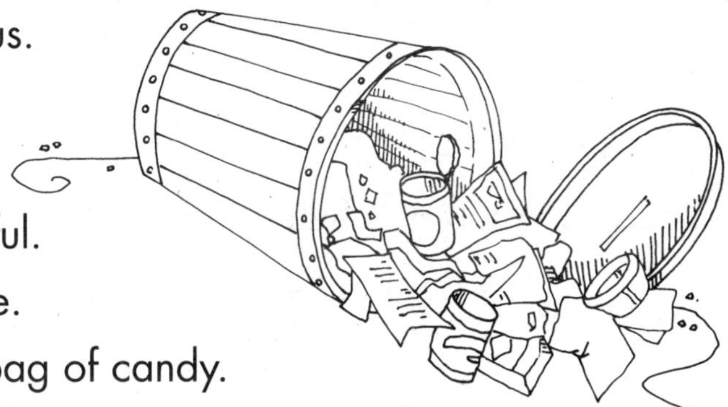

That backyard deck was unvarnished.

Jenna's batting abilities are poor.

The sunburn across my shoulders is painful.

The dent from the cricket ball was sizable.

Tarun will feel sick if he eats that whole bag of candy.

Lal's back was sore from shovelling sand into the sandbox.

Mrs. Mary was enraged when she saw what those cats did to her garbage.

Vineet and I were unhappy with our performance on the tennis courts.

The twins were tired after swimming all afternoon.

Helping Mr. Gopal in the garden all day became boring.

The canoe trip was enjoyable.

That girl watching the otters is captivated by their antics.

That photograph is more breathtaking than your last one.

Grandmother was enchanted with the flowers we picked for her.

Review Work

Write a D above each demonstrative adjective.

Draft Book

Write 10 sentences that use linking verbs and predicate adjectives. Draw an arrow from each predicate adjective to the subject it tells more about.

Name ______________________________

Take Your Pick — predicate adjectives and nouns

Predicate adjectives and predicate nouns follow linking verbs. They tell something about the subject.

Underline the linking verbs. Circle each predicate adjective and each predicate noun. Write *PA* for predicate adjective or *PN* for predicate noun.

_________ Fireflies are fascinating insects.

_________ A galaxy is a group of stars and all the planets that surround them.

_________ Their cabin is cosy.

_________ Ajit is my lab partner.

_________ My jaw is hurting from chewing so much gum.

_________ The book is becoming more interesting.

_________ Your idea is creative.

_________ A driver is a golf club.

_________ That pumpkin is absolutely huge.

_________ Arya was thrilled to be voted class representative.

_________ Our puppy is excited to go for a walk.

_________ Numismatics is the hobby of coin collecting.

_________ Imran was happy to begin reading the new book.

Review Work

Draw an arrow from each predicate adjective or predicate noun to the simple subject it tells more about.

Draft Book

Write 10 sentences that use linking verbs and predicate adjectives or nouns. Draw an arrow from each predicate adjective or noun to the subject it tells more about.

Name ______________________________

Explain It

appositives

An appositive is a word or phrase that explains, identifies or gives information about another word. It comes after the word and usually is enclosed in a set of commas. At the end of a sentence, an appositive is enclosed by a comma and the ending punctuation.

example: My paper, **the one due tomorrow**, is done.

Circle each appositive. Draw an arrow to the noun it modifies.

Lake Superior, one of the Great Lakes of North America, is the largest freshwater lake in the world.

Manatees, aquatic mammals, are very gentle creatures.

Manu and Vipin watched the comets, masses of ice and rock, shimmer across the sky.

Chambered nautiluses, living fossils, live in the Indian and South Pacific Oceans.

Speculation exists that water, a beverage needed for life, may be frozen on the moon.

Ludwig van Beethoven, a deaf musician, conducted the first performance of his Ninth Symphony.

Marie Curie, the only person to receive the Nobel Prize in both chemistry and physics, worked with radioactive materials.

Pappu, the neighbour's dog, loves tomatoes.

Monarchs, migrating butterflies, winter in Mexico.

Spiders, members of the arachnid family, are not insects.

Varun's family canoed around Andman Islands, a group of islands in the Bay of Bangal.

Harish works with an electron microscope, a device used to see minute objects.

Review Work

Underline the complete subjects in the sentences. If the appositive modifies the simple subject, it is part of the complete subject.

Draft Book

Write 10 sentences using appositives.

Name ______________________________

It Was Done to Whom? direct objects

A direct object is the noun or pronoun that receives the action of the verb. It is located in the complete predicate. To locate the direct object, find the verb. Find a noun after the verb that answers *whom* or *what*. If a verb is acting on the noun, the noun is the direct object.

example: The ball hit Mini.

verb (hit) *noun* (Mini)

Mini is the direct object because the ball hit or acted on her.

example: I sent Shad some money.

verb (sent) *nouns* (Shad, money)

Money is the direct object because the money was sent, not Shad.

Underline the verbs. Circle the direct objects.

The courtyard fountain continuously gushed water.

Leena frequently chews gum.

The anxious filly kicked the stall door.

Monika handed Jacob her paper.

Roma stowed the luggage in the overhead bin.

The heavy box squashed my foot.

Deepa offered her chocolate cupcake to Rekha.

The children broke the new vase.

Rosa cancelled her subscription to the magazine.

Yasmeen catches a yellow butterfly.

The hot chicken soup burnt Arun's tongue.

Vidu toasted a potato over the campfire.

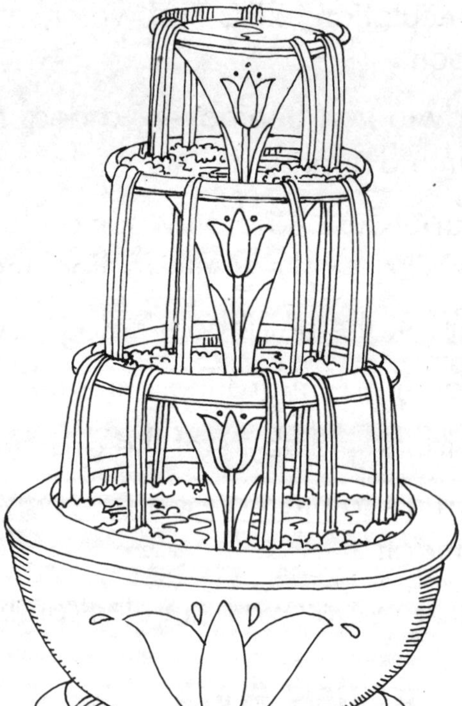

Review Work

Underline the simple subjects with yellow.

Draft Book

Write 10 sentences using direct objects. Circle each direct object.

Name ______________________________

It Was Done for Whom? — indirect objects

An indirect object is the noun or pronoun that answers to whom or for whom (for what). It is located in the complete predicate and usually comes between the verb and the direct object.

example: Renu handed **Hari** a rupee.

verb *indirect object* *direct object*

Hari is the indirect object because the rupee was handed to him.

Underline the verbs once. Underline the direct objects twice. Circle the indirect objects.

José gave the struggling puppy a bath.

Peter wished his grandmother a happy birthday.

Rahul gave Aman the tire swing.

The waiter handed Kartik his burger platter.

Kamla, the girl who sits back there, offered Tommy her pencil.

Aunt Mia knitted Jagjit a new, yellow scarf.

Mr. Thomas gave the chair a coat of varnish.

The first graders sent Santa lengthy letters in November.

The new neighbour made our family stir-fry.

Renuka saved Rahul some sweet corn.

Shan sent his friends invitations to his dance party.

Alice served her family iced lemonade.

Lata throws Sajan her beach towel.

Albert will save Jayant a seat on the bus after school.

Zohra lent Mary her orange umbrella with the polished wood handle.

Review Work

Write an *SS* above the simple subject in each sentence.

Draft Book

Write 10 sentences using indirect objects. Circle the indirect object in each sentence.

Name ______________________________

Here They Are

prepositions

A preposition is a word or group of words that shows a relationship between two words in the sentence. It can tell where something is, where something is going, when something happens, or the relationship between a noun or pronoun and another word. Compound prepositions are multiple prepositions used together.

Single Prepositions Include:

aboard, about, above, across, after, against, along, alongside, among, around, as, at, before, behind, below, beneath, beside, besides, between, beyond, but, by, despite, down, during, except, for, from, in, inside, into, like, near, of, off, on, onto, out, outside, over, past, round, since, through, throughout, till, to, towards, under, underneath, until, up, upon, with, within, without

Compound Prepositions Include:

according to, ahead of, along with, as for, away from, because of, by way of, due to, except for, in addition to, in back of, in case of, in front of, in regard to, in spite of, instead of, out of, up to, with the exception of

Write three sentences using single prepositions and three sentences using compound prepositions.

____

____

____

____

____

____

Review Work

Circle the prepositions in the sentences. Underline the nouns with yellow and the verbs with blue.

Draft Book

Choose 10 prepositions from the lists above and write unique phrases, such as "aboard our flying saucer one night." Use these phrases as creative story starters.

Name ____________________

Identifying Prepositions

prepositional phrases

A preposition is a word or group of words that shows a relationship between two words in the sentence. It can tell where something is, where something is going, when something happens, or the relationship between a noun or pronoun and another word. Compound prepositions are multiple prepositions used together.

A prepositional phrase begins with a preposition and ends with a noun or pronoun. The noun or pronoun in a prepositional phrase is called the object of the preposition. A preposition always has an object. If the word does not have an object, it is not acting as a preposition. A sentence can have more than one prepositional phrase.

example: The book **on the desk** is mine.

preposition (on) *object* (desk)

Box the prepositions. Circle the objects of the prepositions. Underline the prepositional phrases.

The Arabian mare thundered around the corral.

Mani's sunset photograph is hanging on our living room wall.

Aruna ordered a thick milkshake instead of an ice-cream cone.

Rita hugged her horse with all her strength.

Ria walked carefully around the edge of the pond.

The washed grapes are in the blue bowl.

Madhu slept with her thumb in her mouth.

Mr. Mohan has a bag of candies in his desk drawer.

The box of books is located behind the door.

The jar of homemade pineapple jam did not last long.

We are renting the cottage near the dock.

Bala wiped up the spill with a paper towel.

Review Work

Write an *SS* above the simple subject in each sentence.

Draft Book

Write 10 sentences using prepositional phrases. Underline the prepositions.

Name ______________________________

Tell About Nouns

adjective prepositional phrases

Prepositional phrases show relationships. Prepositional phrases can modify nouns or verbs. An adjective prepositional phrase shows a relationship between a noun and the object of the preposition. It modifies a noun or pronoun just like a one-word adjective.

example: Rohit ate a huge bowl of badam halwa.

noun adjective prepositional phrase

Circle each adjective prepositional phrase. Draw an arrow to the noun or pronoun it modifies.

The candle on the piano is vanilla scented.

Use that container of fertiliser to feed the plants.

The books from the library must be returned today.

Anna likes bread with butter and mango syrup.

That radish in the salad is very spicy.

The boy near the slide helped me pick up trash.

The horse with the green saddle blanket won the prize.

Students throughout the school want a longer lunch period.

The girl with chicken pox ate lunch with my sister yesterday.

Julie ordered marble cake with Bavarian cream filling and chocolate frosting.

Sai shovelled the end of the driveway.

The red scarf around my neck was knitted by Prem.

Our class will clean up the mess around the cricket field.

Review Work

Underline the object of the preposition in each sentence.

Draft Book

Write 10 sentences using adjective prepositional phrases. Underline each preposition and draw an arrow to the noun or pronoun it modifies.

Name ______________________________

Which Verb?

adjective prepositional phrases and noun-verb agreement

When an adjective prepositional phrase modifies the simple subject, the subject (not the object of the preposition) must agree with the verb.

example: A can of guavas falls on the floor. (yes)
A can of guavas fall on the floor. (no)
The verb must agree with the simple subject *can*.

Underline the simple subjects once. Underline the prepositional phrases twice. Circle the correct verbs.

The buttons on her sweater (is, are) wooden.

The dog with many spots (growl, growls) at anyone entering that yard.

The people throughout the area (want, wants) this road to have a four-way stop.

The girl with braces (brushes, brush) her teeth twice a day.

The parking places outside the mall (need, needs) ploughing.

The couch with green and brown stripes (is, are) comfortable.

A bucket of mangoes (cost, costs) twenty rupees.

That pack of pencils (is, are) inexpensive.

The sweaters in that display (fit, fits) me.

Many marbles in that game (are, is) matching.

The pictures of the zoo trip (are, is) developed.

Many socks in her drawer (do, does) not match.

The guinea pig with black spots (need, needs) a good home.

The videos on the bottom shelf (need, needs) to be returned.

That banana with many dark spots (is, are) destined for banana bread.

Review Work

Draw a box around the object of each preposition.

Draft Book

Write 10 sentences using adjective prepositional phrases. Make the simple subjects and verbs agree.

Name ________________________________

Tell About Verbs

adverb prepositional phrases

Prepositional phrases show relationships. Prepositional phrases can modify nouns or verbs. An adverb prepositional phrase modifies the verb. It tells how, where, when or to what extent something happens just like a one-word adverb.

Underline each adverb prepositional phrase. Tell how it modifies the verb by writing *how, where, when* or *what* on the line.

______________ The trip photos are in the album.

______________ David and Walter walked to the store.

______________ The batsman played beyond his average performance.

______________ During yesterday's thunderstorm, the power went out.

______________ The Girl Scout troop will sleep at Ms. Alice's house Friday night.

______________ Without any complaining, Jameela cleaned her room.

______________ Sweety must be home before 7:00 p.m.

______________ Geno will put that can into the recycle bin.

______________ Their family vacations in June.

______________ My dad ate ice cream and cookies until he was full.

______________ Dev and I finished the project with assistance.

______________ He went straight to his room.

______________ Shelly found many monarch caterpillars on the milkweed plants.

______________ We will visit our cousins over the holiday break.

______________ On Saturday night, we saw the full moon.

______________ The neighbourhood children had a football match despite the scorching temperatures.

Review Work

Underline the simple subjects with yellow.

Draft Book

Write 10 sentences using a variety of adverb prepositional phrases.

Name ______________________________

The Difference — adverb or adverb prepositional phrases

Many of the same words can be used as adverbs or to begin adverb prepositional phrases. A prepositional phrase always has an object of the preposition.

adverb: The dog ran **around**.

preposition: The dog ran **around** the house.

Identify each word in bold type. Write adverb or preposition.

______________ The beaver swam **to** his underwater door.

______________ Aamir always flosses **between** his teeth.

______________ The coals are hot; you can put your hot dog **in**.

______________ The sails billowed **during** the boat ride.

______________ The bear crawled **in** his den and went to sleep.

______________ Pran sat **nearby** as the air show continued.

______________ Dolphins live **underneath** the ocean.

______________ When the rain started, we went **inside**.

______________ The crowd clapped as the band passed **by**.

______________ My little sister leaned **against** my leg while we were reading.

______________ Do not put the napkin on the plate; put it **underneath**.

______________ Ritu and Leena walked **along** the edge of the dune.

______________ The snow came **down** and covered the ground.

Review Work

Underline the prepositional phrases. Circle the object of each preposition.

Draft Book

Write 10 sentences using adverbs and adverb prepositional phrases.

Name ______________________________

A Group of Words

adverb or adverb prepositional phrases

Many of the same words can be used as adverbs or to begin adverb prepositional phrases. A prepositional phrase always has an object of the preposition.

adverb: The ship sank **below**.
preposition: The ship sank **below** the ocean.

Box each adverb and preposition. Underline each prepositional phrase.

Kamal made the mixture for his cow.

They can leave for the park whenever.

The power has been out since Monday.

At three o'clock, we will go outside.

They are not moving until tomorrow.

Natasha recited her poem for the class.

We finished the papers before.

He came inside for a snack.

Bijoy set the rake against the garage.

A bluebird nest is in the tree.

We will stop for ice cream after the programme.

Review Work

Draw an arrow from each adverb or adverb prepositional phrase to the verb it modifies.

Draft Book

Write 10 sentences using prepositions as adverbs and as adverb prepositional phrases. Identify how the preposition is used in each sentence: ADV = adverb and AP = adverb prepositional phrase.

Name ______________________________

Which Is Which? adjective and adverb prepositional phrases

Prepositional phrases show relationships. Prepositional phrases can modify nouns or verbs. An adjective prepositional phrase modifies the noun. An adverb prepositional phrase modifies the verb.

Underline the prepositional phrases. Write *Adj* above each adjective prepositional phrase and *Adv* above each adverb prepositional phrase.

Dinesh put the night crawlers into the bucket.

The bread in that bag is stale.

The beekeeper delivered his bees to the fruit orchard.

Talia reads a book in the morning.

The cow from that farm is standing in the middle of the road.

The Milky Way is only one of many galaxies in the universe.

The crystal clips held her hair off her forehead.

The box of chocolates melted in the trunk of the hot car.

Raj delivered the jar of homemade apricot jam.

On Monday morning, Renu jogged five miles.

Our team won the match despite playing on their field.

Amber walked through the door of the gym.

Make a turn off this road at the next stop sign.

Rina swam across the pool to the deep end.

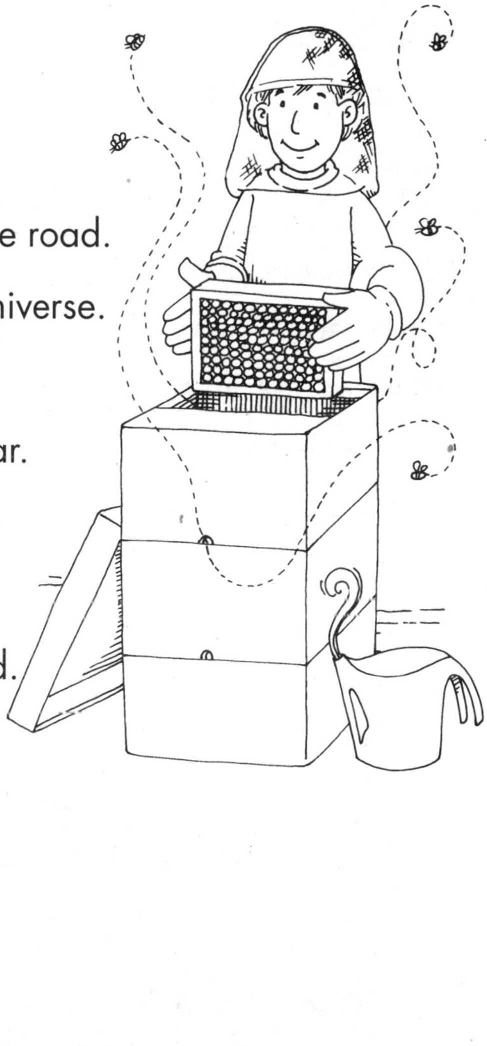

Review Work

Underline the verbs with blue.

Draft Book

Write 10 sentences using prepositional phrases. Write *Adj* above each adjective prepositional phrase and *Adv* above each adverb prepositional phrase.

Name ________________________________

We Sound the Same

homophones

Homophones are words that sound alike but are spelt differently and have different meanings.

Write the correct homophone on each line.

its: possessive pronoun **it's:** contraction for it is

__________________ too late to go to the movie now.

The cottage has __________________ own beach access.

__________________ top is scratched.

Monica believes __________________ too hot to drive to the library.

there: location word **their:** possessive pronoun **they're:** contraction for they are

__________________ house is on the cul-de-sac at the end of the street.

__________________ lots of fun to play games with.

Matthew and Jay went __________________ for a cookout.

Roma really likes __________________ goats.

At the ice-cream shop, __________________ having a two-for-one special today.

Latika will rest __________________ before biking the last six miles.

your: possessive pronoun **you're:** contraction for you are

__________________ visiting the zoo with us this Wednesday.

Do you like __________________ new hot tub?

I'm sorry __________________ not able to come to the cookout.

whose: interrogative pronoun **who's:** contraction for who is

__________________ were you planning to paint first?

There is no name on this paper; __________________ is it?

The store wants to hire the student __________________ the most reliable.

Review Work

Underline the nouns with yellow.

Draft Book

Write three sentences for each homophone on this page.

Name ____________________

Questions, Questions

interrogative sentences

An interrogative sentence asks a question. It ends with a question mark.

Write interrogative sentences that would be answered by each of the following statements. Put an uppercase letter at the beginning and a question mark at the end of each.

interrogative sentence: ____________________

It is on Friday.

interrogative sentence: ____________________

They are over there.

interrogative sentence: ____________________

It is over six feet tall.

interrogative sentence: ____________________

It must have been him.

interrogative sentence: ____________________

It is hers.

interrogative sentence: ____________________

It is in Tamil Nadu.

interrogative sentence: ____________________

They live in the rain forest.

interrogative sentence: ____________________

It is less than three kilos.

Review Work

Underline the pronouns in the sentences with red.

Draft Book

Write 10 interrogative sentences and answers. Include pronouns in your answers.

Name ______________________________

Science Class

interrogative and declarative sentences

An interrogative sentence asks a question and ends with a question mark. A declarative sentence tells something and ends with a full stop.

Put the correct punctuation mark at the end of each sentence.

matter is anything that has mass and takes up space ☐

solids, liquids and gases are the three states of matter ☐

did you that know solids and liquids can combine to produce a gas ☐

we put baking soda, a solid, into an empty aquarium ☐

we also put in five candles at varying heights ☐

then, we added vinegar, a liquid ☐

can you predict what happened ☐

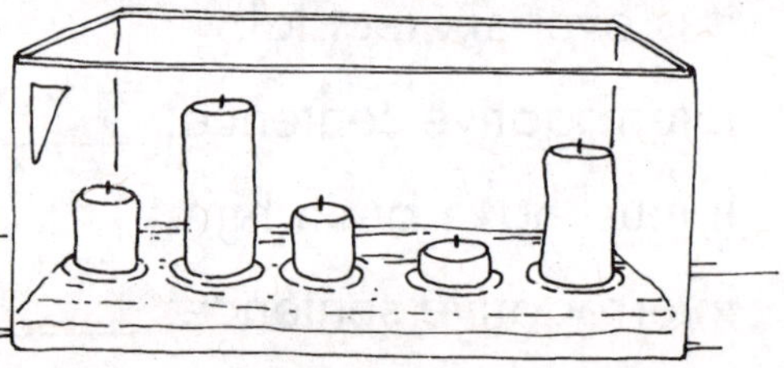

the baking soda and vinegar combined in a chemical reaction making carbon dioxide, a gas ☐

the evidence was the candles ☐

beginning with the shortest candle, the candles went out, one by one ☐

mrs. arora used a bubble wand to blow bubbles into the aquarium ☐

do you know what happened ☐

the bubbles floated right where the carbon dioxide and room air met ☐

carbon dioxide is heavier than room air ☐

the candles and bubbles showed where the layer of carbon dioxide ended ☐

Review Work

Review sentences for words that should start with uppercase letters. Cross out the lowercase letters and write the uppercase letters above them.

Draft Book

Write six interrogative and six declarative sentences. End each sentence with the correct punctuation mark.

Name ______________________________

Wow! exclamatory sentences

An exclamatory sentence shows strong feelings and ends with an exclamation mark.

Rewrite each exclamatory sentence. Put uppercase letters where they belong and exclamation marks at the ends.

i passed the science test

____

we got an invitation to the party

____

the moon looks incredible tonight

____

hey, don't step on my books

____

this ice cream is fantastic

____

don't throw my homework away

____

jay won the contest

____

Review Work

Choose one sentence from above and draw a star next to it. If that sentence is the answer, what is the question?

____

Draft Book

Write 10 exclamatory sentences. End each sentence with an exclamation mark.

Name ____________________________________

With Feeling
imperative sentences

A sentence that tells you what to do or gives you a command is called an imperative sentence. Most imperative sentences end with full stops. Occasionally, a command is given with great feeling. In this case, an exclamation mark is used. The same command can end with either a full stop or an exclamation mark depending on the situation.

example: Sit down.⟶Mom is asking you to sit down to dinner.
Sit down!⟶A small child is standing on a rocking chair, and it is about to tip over.

Read the situations. Put the correct punctuation at the end of each imperative sentence.

Stop that ☐ A friend is tapping her pencil.

Stop that ☐ Your brother is hitting your bruised shoulder.

Wash your hands ☐ Someone touched poison ivy.

Wash your hands ☐ It is dinnertime.

Put water on it ☐ A fire started in the trash can.

Put water on it ☐ The soil in the plant is beginning to dry.

Move ☐ Your friend is lounging on the couch, and you would like to share.

Move ☐ The bull has spotted your friend in his pasture and is racing towards her.

Get your dad ☐ It is time for dinner.

Get your dad ☐ The ladder fell down, and Mom is stuck on the roof.

Review Work

Give the situations for these two imperative sentences.

Run! ____________________________________

Run. ____________________________________

Draft Book

Write 10 imperative sentences. Begin each with an uppercase letter. End some sentences with full stops and some with exclamation marks. Describe each situation.

Name ______________________________

You, You, You

subject of imperative sentences

A sentence that tells you what to do or gives you a command is called an imperative sentence. Most imperative sentences end with a full stop. An imperative sentence looks like a complete predicate. The complete subject is *you*. *You* is implied, which means that since the speaker is talking to you, it is understood that *you* is the subject, even though the word *you* isn't always written.

Underline the complete predicates. Circle the simple predicates.

Brush your teeth after every meal.

Turn off the television so you can get ready for bed.

Call me as soon as you arrive.

Don't bring food into your bedroom.

Put the return address in the upper, left corner of the envelope.

Drink plenty of water so you won't get dehydrated.

Change the interrogative sentences to imperative sentences.

Will you pass the salt and pepper?

____

Can you write Adnan a thank-you note this afternoon?

____

Will you read the book and turn in a report by Monday?

____

Review Work

Change one imperative sentence from the top of the page to an interrogative sentence.

____

Draft Book

Write 10 imperative sentences. End each sentence with a full stop.

Name ______________________________

New Pool

sentence types

There are four main types of sentences. A declarative sentence tells something and ends with a full stop. An interrogative sentence asks a question and ends with a question mark. An exclamatory sentence shows strong feelings and ends with an exclamation mark. An imperative sentence is a command. The subject *you* is implied. It usually ends in a full stop, but can end in an exclamation mark.

Write *declarative, interrogative, exclamatory* or *imperative* on each line.

_______________ We have the plans for putting a pool in our backyard.

_______________ Would you like to see them?

_______________ Don't touch the plans with dirty hands, please.

_______________ Look right here.

_______________ Can you see this area?

_______________ It is the deep end.

_______________ It's huge!

_______________ They will begin to dig the hole for the pool next week.

_______________ It will take three weeks until it is finished.

_______________ Put your finger on the large area here.

_______________ That whole area will be the deck.

_______________ Did you know that we will have to build a fence, too?

_______________ It has to be five feet tall for safety reasons.

_______________ I can hardly wait!

Review Work

Underline the complete subjects once and the complete predicates twice.

Draft Book

Write four declarative, four interrogative, four exclamatory and four imperative sentences. End each sentence with the correct punctuation mark.

Name ______________________________

To + Verb

infinitives

Infinitives are present tense verbs that are usually preceded by the word *to*. An infinitive can act as a noun, adjective or adverb.

Circle the infinitives.

We need to water the plants.

To be outstanding was Maria's goal.

To open the jar takes muscles.

You will need to remove the plastic liner.

Courage is needed to enter the haunted mansion.

To grill outside is best.

We want to enjoy the movie without a lot of extra noise.

Everyone would like to drink from the colder drinking fountain.

Ajit and Preeti want to show the class how to make chapatis.

We will be ready to leave when all of the toys are picked up.

The buds on the yellow flowers are beginning to open.

Dad has to run to the store for more nails.

We have to clean up this mess.

Sandeep can't wait to go on vacation in December.

The baby began to crawl on the floor.

We must wait until this afternoon to swim in the pool.

You need five tokens to play the arcade games.

Daily teeth brushing helps to keep plaque from forming cavities.

Manu wants to have that candy bar.

Regular practice is needed to excel at basketball.

Review Work

Write an *SS* above the simple subject in each sentence.

Draft Book

Write 10 sentences using infinitives. Underline the infinitives.

Name ______________________________

He or Him?

more about pronouns

Pronouns take the place of nouns. Subject pronouns take the place of subject nouns. Object pronouns take the place of nouns used as objects and are found in the complete predicate. Possessive pronouns take the place of possessive nouns. The possessive pronoun *its* does not have an apostrophe.

subject pronouns: I, you, he, she, we, they, it
object pronouns: me, you, her, him, them, us, it
possessive pronouns:
  before a noun: my, your, his, her, its, our, their
  after a linking verb: mine, yours, his, hers, its, ours, theirs

Circle the correct pronouns.

Sara and Bonnie took (they, them) to the matinee.

After the party, (us, we) helped clean the room.

Rupa helped (she, her) find the lens to (her, hers) glasses.

(I, me) planted many seeds in (our, ours) garden.

Will (you, your) come with (I, me) to (their, theirs) house?

Joy loaned (he, his) new, cricket bat to (she, her).

Did (her, she) blame (we, us) for the broken window?

Tania will help Manoj and (I, me) look for (it, its).

(We, Us) can build (it, its) over there in (your, yours) big tree.

Omar and (I, me) took an art course this summer.

(I, me) went with (he, him) to the library.

(They, Them) promised to come with (we, us) to the arcade across town.

The elephant tossed water on (their, theirs) clothing and mud on (our, ours).

Anna, (she, you) have (your, yours) own markers; quit borrowing (my, mine).

Review Work

Underline the prepositional phrases in the sentences.

Draft Book

Find a page of writing in your Draft Book and search for pronouns. Underline them with red. Make corrections where necessary.

Name ________________________________

This Is It

demonstrative pronouns

Pronouns take the place of nouns. The four demonstrative pronouns are the same as the four demonstrative adjectives: *this, that, these* and *those*. A demonstrative pronoun takes the place of the noun rather than describes it.

singular (located nearby):	this	singular (located a distance away):	that
plural (located nearby):	these	plural (located a distance away):	those

Circle the demonstrative pronouns.

This will do a better job cleaning the windows than that.

These will taste better on the salad.

When it is raining, those are the better boots to wear.

On your nose, that is the sunscreen to use.

When did those become fashionable?

In gym class, that is the most exciting game to play.

Those belong to Rasheed; put them in his desk.

During summer break, that is the place to meet people.

Those are her best recipes.

Circle the demonstrative words. Write *DP* for demonstrative pronoun or *DA* for demonstrative adjective above each word.

This is the watch belonging in that display case.

That is the best rake to use when those leaves fall.

This must be added to it before there is enough hose to water that area of the garden.

That is not the correct method to use when solving this problem.

Those are the people that obnoxious child came with.

This summer we will use that when picking those mangoes.

Review Work

Underline other pronouns in the sentences with red.

Draft Book

Write 10 sentences using demonstrative pronouns. Write *DP* above each demonstrative pronoun.

Name ______________________________

Someone Can

indefinite pronouns

Pronouns take the place of nouns. Indefinite pronouns refer to nouns in a general way. Indefinite pronouns include the following words: *all, another, any, anybody, anyone, anything, both, each, either, everybody, everyone, everything, few, little, many, more, most, much, neither, nobody, none, no one, nothing, one, ones, other, others, several, some, somebody, someone* and *something*.

Circle the indefinite pronouns.

Many will come to the museum this summer.

One came to the feeder this morning, and another came last night.

A few excited ones got the crowd going.

Only a few registered, but several arrived on the first day of camp.

I think somebody should clean up the marbles and game pieces.

Gautam and Mudit are at the door; either can mow the yard.

If someone gets home before me, he can put dinner in the oven.

Fruits and vegetables are delicious; each is good for a healthy, growing body.

Any who enter may choose their routes.

Jessie really wanted both of them.

No one chose to help with the clean-up activities.

Some have blue tags and others have red tags.

Nothing can be done about the misplaced invitation.

All of the leaves will fall from the tree at the end of summer.

Anyone can come to the amusement park if he is accompanied by an adult.

Several swam downstream into the lake.

Review Work

Underline the prepositional phrases.

Draft Book

Write 10 sentences using indefinite pronouns. Underline them with red.

Name ____________________________________

I Myself

intensive and reflexive pronouns

An intensive pronoun draws attention to or intensifies a noun or a pronoun. The intensive pronouns are:

singular: myself, yourself, himself, herself, itself
plural: ourselves, yourselves, themselves

These pronouns can also be reflexive pronouns. A reflexive pronoun "reflects" back to the subject of a sentence.

examples: intensive pronoun: Mr. Ganesh **himself** carved the cake.
reflexive pronoun: Salma helped **herself** to the cake.

Circle the intensive and reflexive pronouns in the sentences below. Write *IP* for intensive pronoun or *RP* for reflexive pronoun on each line.

__________ Vineet told himself it had to be a huge mistake.

__________ Deepa baked the biscuits and made the tea herself.

__________ Pamela and Anand introduced themselves to the new teacher.

__________ I timed myself to see how long it would take to walk to school.

__________ Last night, Maya and I completed the puzzle ourselves.

__________ The winner, Atul himself, donated fifty books.

__________ Soumi reminded herself that she had to be home by six o'clock.

__________ The bees themselves saved the farmer from loss.

__________ Soumi and I helped ourselves to that chocolate ice cream.

__________ The ants helped themselves to some of our picnic.

__________ I myself took that piece of pizza.

__________ That class themselves sold over one thousand candy bars.

__________ The pigeon helped itself to birdseed and the sliced orange.

Review Work

Underline the simple subjects once and the simple predicates twice.

Draft Book

Write 10 sentences using a variety of intensive and reflexive pronouns.

Name ________________________________

To or With Whom

interrogative pronouns

Interrogative pronouns are used to ask questions. Sometimes they begin interrogative sentences. The five interrogative pronouns are: *what*, *which*, *who*, *whom* and *whose*. *Who* is used like a subject pronoun; *whom* is used like an object pronoun. If these words are not being used in place of nouns, they are not interrogative pronouns.

Circle the interrogative pronouns in the sentences below.

I need to know which will fit you.

Which did you buy, the yellow or green one?

Big Store has what you need to finish the tree house.

The teacher knows with whom each person is working.

Whose are those platters of sandwiches?

What are they bringing to the holiday picnic?

The class planned with whom each student would read.

Mom wants to know who put her finger into the cake's frosting.

Whose should we enter in the city competition?

Who was talking before?

To whom were you speaking on the phone?

With whom do you plan to ride home?

We don't know whose those are.

Neha knows which has won the contest.

Nandita knows which will produce the largest blooms.

Sajida doesn't know who will take her ticket.

Which did Arun choose as his puppy?

Review Work

Change one declarative sentence from the top of the page to an interrogative sentence.

____

Draft Book

Write 10 sentences using interrogative pronouns.

Name ______________________________

Past the Verb

object pronouns

An object pronoun takes the place of a noun found in the complete predicate. It can replace the direct object, indirect object or object of the preposition. Object pronouns are: *me*, *you*, *her*, *him*, *them*, *us* and *it*.

Replace each word in bold type with an object pronoun. Write the correct pronoun on the line.

Rashmi wanted **the new green ruler** to bring to school. ____________

Asha gave **Mrs. Kumar** the envelope with her lunch money. ____________

Tarun sprayed the hose at **Joy and Neeta**. ____________

Mrs. Nath brought **Ajay and me** to the cricket field. ____________

The dog chewed **Aunt Rama's new green rug**. ____________

The shoes with red laces were bought by **Tinku and Dilip**. ____________

Bobbi and Sweety gave **the miniature goat** some food pellets. ____________

Rakesh pushed **Sagar** on the swings. ____________

Nitya bought ice cream bars for **Vineet and me**. ____________

Suman danced on the stage with **Peter**. ____________

Sharad, get onto **the cycle** so we can go downhill. ____________

A new family just moved in across from **Sri Lanka**. ____________

Use the object pronouns *me* and *you* to write two sentences below. Remember to place each object pronoun in the complete predicate.

example: The bright sun gave me a headache.

____

____

Review Work

Write *DO* for direct object, *IO* for indirect object or *OP* for object of the preposition above each word in bold type in the sentences.

Draft Book

Write a story about a picnic in the park using object pronouns. Underline the pronouns with red.

Name ________________________________

It Must Be Mine

possessive pronouns

Possessive pronouns take the place of possessive nouns. They can be used before a noun or after a linking verb. The possessive pronoun *its* does not have an apostrophe.

before a noun: my, your, his, her, its, our, their
after a linking verb: mine, yours, his, hers, its, ours, theirs

example: My brush is on the table. That brush is **mine.**

Circle each possessive pronoun. Draw an arrow to the noun it modifies.

Their mom travels around the state on business.

Our house is near the library.

Its handle is loose.

The black dog under that bush is mine.

Her socks are in the middle drawer.

We went to the musical with his parents.

The house with the pool is his.

My friend asked my opinion about which bike to buy.

The salami and cheese sandwich is hers.

Their wooded backyard is a great place to play.

Her older cousin is staying at their house for a week.

The trophy has its own shelf.

His old bunk bed was given to his younger brother.

Review Work

Underline the complete subjects in the sentences. If the possessive noun modifies the simple subject, it is part of the complete subject.

Draft Book

Write sentences using the list of possessive pronouns on this page. Use each possessive pronoun at least once.

Name ______________________________

Throw Some Out

contractions

A contraction is two words that are put together to form one word. An apostrophe replaces the missing letters. Many contractions are formed using pronouns and other words. The following letters are left with the apostrophe when a contraction is made.

'll when adding *will* (that**'ll**)
'd when adding *would* or *had* (we**'d**)
's when adding *is* or *has* (she**'s**)
're when adding *are* (we**'re**)
've when adding *have* (I**'ve**)

Write the contractions.

I + would =	________________	he + will =	________________
it + is =	________________	what + is =	________________
they + would =	________________	they + will =	________________

Write the words that form the contractions.

he'd =	________________	I'll =	________________
there've =	________________	I'm =	________________
we'd =	________________	she'll =	________________

Circle each contraction. Write the words it replaces on the line.

________________ Do you think they've gone to the game without us?
________________ Kris and John think they're not invited to the party.
________________ Neha said she'd bring a blanket to the camp out.
________________ Has Mrs. Dutt decided who's making the announcement today?
________________ There's enough time to finish the card.
________________ I think I'll put the new video on the top shelf.
________________ Here's the key we looked for all morning!

Review Work
Underline the nouns with yellow.

Draft Book
Write a sentence using each contraction from this page.

Name ______________________________

Did Not!

contractions: not

A contraction is two words that are put together to form one word. An apostrophe replaces the missing letters. *Not* is a word that forms contractions with many helping or linking verbs. In contractions, the o in *not* is replaced with an apostrophe.

example: did + not = didn't

The contraction for *will not* is an exception: will + not = won't.

Circle each contraction. Write the two words that formed it on the line.

________________ We aren't planning to attend the football game tonight.

________________ The plan itself isn't to sit around and do nothing.

________________ Renuka wasn't in the band room this morning.

________________ Tara shouldn't have to do that by herself.

________________ The children mustn't put their dirty hands on the sliding door.

________________ That table can't take the load of all those bricks.

________________ Jayan hadn't done his homework.

________________ Alex wouldn't take a snack without asking.

________________ Sara, Gopi and Suma weren't at the park yesterday.

________________ The mail carrier hasn't driven down Mannadi Street yet.

________________ Mika, our new puppy, didn't want to sleep.

________________ Alisha and I haven't done our morning chores.

________________ Varun doesn't want to eat pizza.

________________ Many won't arrive until after the food booth opens.

________________ Omar didn't have anyone to help him.

________________ The squirrels couldn't get onto the new bird feeder.

Review Work

Underline each pronoun with red.

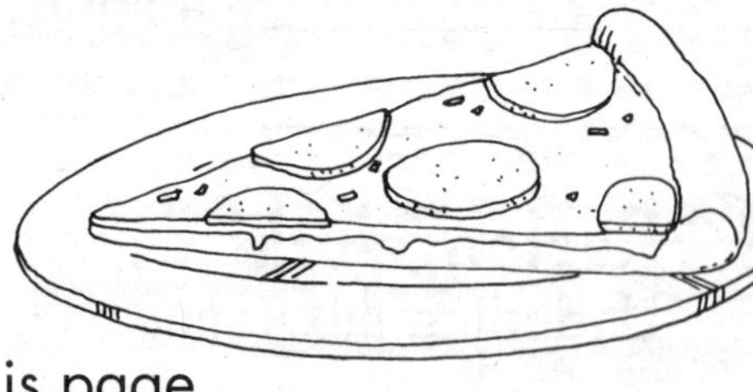

Draft Book

Write a sentence using each contraction from this page.

Name ______________________________

Combining Sentences

coordinating conjunctions

Sentences can be combined when their ideas are the same. Related sentences can be joined with coordinating conjunctions. There are seven coordinating conjunctions: *and, nor, but, for, yet, so* and *or.*

examples: Alex plays tennis. + Alex plays basketball. =
Alex plays tennis and basketball.
Anika slept on the plane. + Anika did not sleep on the train. =
Anika slept on the plane but not on the train.

Combine each set of sentences using a coordinating conjunction. Write the new sentence on the line.

Devan went swimming in the pool. Devan did not go swimming in the lake.

____

The flowers need to be watered. The flowers need to be fertilised.

____

Julie remembered her backpack. Julie did not remember her lunch.

____

We can watch the movie. We can play a game.

____

I did not buy candy. I didn't buy chips.

____

The squirrel jumped on the bird feeder. The squirrel ate the birdseed.

____

Latika likes broccoli. Latika likes cauliflower.

____

Review Work

Circle the coordinating conjunctions.

Draft Book

Write five pairs of sentences that can be combined. Write a combined sentence for each pair.

Name ________________________________

We Did it — compound subjects

Similar sentences can be combined into one simple sentence with a compound subject by using a coordinating conjunction.

example: Dan studied today. + Jack studied today. = Dan and Jack studied today.

Dan studied today. + Jack did not study today. =
Dan but not Jack studied today.

If three or more subjects are combined, use commas to separate them and the conjunction.

example: Dan studied today. + Jack studied today. + Mohit studied today. =
Dan, Jack and Mohit studied today.

Underline the compound subject in each sentence.

Blues, minkes and sperm whales are known as great whales.

The biographies but not the anthologies are on the first shelf.

Joe, Micky, Shiela and Hari play trumpets in the band.

Andy and I bought ice-cream sandwiches.

Blue jays, finches, pigeons and mynahs come daily to the bird feeder.

Use a coordinating conjunction to combine each set of sentences into one sentence with a compound subject. Write each sentence on a line.

Jyotika ate salad. Alia ate salad.

____

Jacob planted the corn. Jeet planted the corn.

____

Dolphins are mammals. Whales are mammals. Elephants are mammals.

____

Review Work

In the combined sentences you wrote, underline the complete subjects once and the complete predicates twice.

Draft Book

Write five sets of sentences containing first nouns that can be combined. Trade with a partner and combine the sentences.

Name ______________________________

Doing Many Things

combining predicates

Similar sentences can be combined into one simple sentence with a compound predicate by using a coordinating conjunction.

example: Jan planted the seeds. + Jan watered the seeds. = Jan planted and watered the seeds.

Underline the compound predicate in each sentence. Circle each coordinating conjunction.

The rocket ignited and blasted off into space.

Balu and Radha washed, vacuumed and waxed the car.

The dog broke the leash and ran away.

The wind whipped the tree's branches and shredded its leaves.

Rajan catches and throws during practice.

Mili whipped and folded the eggs into the batter.

Use a coordinating conjunction to combine each set of sentences into one sentence with a compound predicate. Write each sentence on a line.

Vipin measured the board. Vipin cut the board.

____

Disha swept the floor. Disha mopped the floor. Disha waxed the floor.

____

The kitten pounced on the ball of yarn. The kitten swatted the ball of yarn.

____

Punit screamed on the roller coaster. Punit enjoyed the roller coaster.

____

Review Work

In the combined sentences you wrote, underline the simple subjects once and the simple predicates twice.

Draft Book

Write five sets of sentences whose verbs can be combined. Write a combined sentence for each set.

Name ________________________________

We Can Relate

compound subjects and predicates

Sentences can be combined when their ideas are the same. Related sentences can be joined with coordinating conjunctions.

Circle the coordinating conjunctions. If a sentence has a compound subject write *CS*. If a sentence has a compound predicate write *CP*. If it has both, write *B*.

________ Salmon and walleye swim upstream in that river.

________ Dilip and Sara formed and threw snowballs.

________ Bats and dragonflies eat mosquitoes.

________ Trilok bought cotton candy and ate it.

________ The grapes and apples fell and rolled on the floor.

________ Javed and Akhtar growled at the intruder.

________ The horseflies and mosquitoes irritated and pestered the hikers.

________ Mercury and Venus are between the Sun and Earth.

________ Joe poured and drank the ice water.

________ The cow and its calf live in that pasture.

________ Alok and Ekta held and watched the sparklers.

________ Jupiter and Saturn have rings.

________ The machine copied and collated the reports.

________ Lalit and Dalia have braces.

________ A tape recorder but not a CD player records and plays music.

________ Rohit bit, chewed and swallowed the burger.

________ Jyoti cleaned and filleted the fish.

Review Work

Write an *SS* above each simple subject. Underline the simple predicates with blue.

Draft Book

Write 10 sentences with compound subjects, compound predicates or both.

Name ____________________________

Can I Stand Alone? clauses

A clause is a group of words with a subject and a predicate. An independent clause can stand alone as a sentence.

example: Jan plays cricket.

A dependent clause cannot stand alone; it is used with an independent clause.

example: because he likes the sport (not a sentence)
Jan plays cricket because he likes the sport.

Write *IC* if the group of words is an independent clause. Write *DC* if the group of words is a dependent clause.

________ whenever Dilip gets a pickle

________ everyone teases him

________ jasmine rides her horse Tally

________ so Chand bought a new bat

________ those flowers are blooming early

________ until Lila decides to finish her homework

________ i walked a mile before school

________ since it was thundering and lightning

________ because the bag of candy was unopened

________ kishan chewed three sticks of gum

________ the store closed at six o'clock

________ if Munir orders french fries

________ leena hung the picture on the wall

________ although the power went out

________ the toilet-paper roll is empty

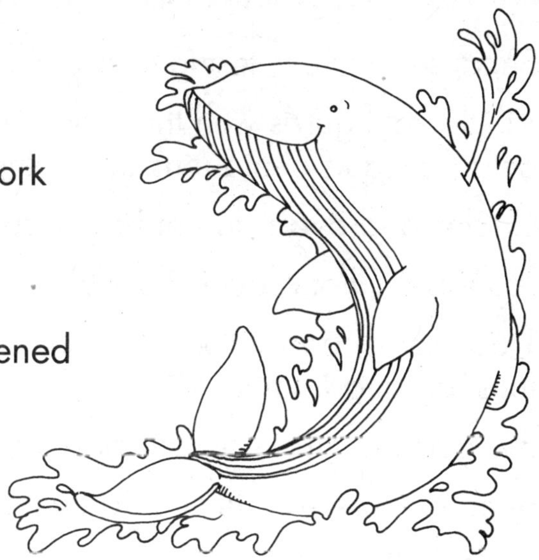

Review Work

Add uppercase letters and punctuation to the sentences above.

Draft Book

Write complete sentences using the dependent clauses above.

Name ______________________________

Geometry

clauses

A clause is a group of words with a subject and a predicate. An independent clause can stand alone.

example: Louis often swims.

A dependent clause cannot stand alone; it is used with an independent clause.

example: because he lives at the beach (not a sentence)
Louis often swims because he lives at the beach.

When a dependent clause is added after an independent clause, no additional punctuation is needed. When a dependent clause is added before an independent clause, a comma is placed between the two clauses.

example: Because he lives at the beach, Louis often swims.

Underline each independent clause once. Underline each dependent clause twice. Add commas where needed.

Because I have a test tomorrow I am studying my geometry.

All closed figures with three or more straight sides are polygons, so triangles, octagons and pentagons are polygons.

Circles and ovals do not have straight sides, so they are not polygons.

A shape is not a quadrilateral unless it has four sides.

Trapezoids, parallelograms, rectangles and squares all have four sides so they must be quadrilaterals.

If a quadrilateral has four parallel sides, it is a parallelogram.

Because a rectangle has parallel sides it must be a parallelogram as well as a quadrilateral.

Review Work

Circle the articles with orange.

Draft Book

Write 10 sentences combining independent and dependent clauses. Use commas when needed.

Name ______________________________

Just a Piece

phrases and clauses

A phrase is a group of words that does not have a subject and predicate. A clause is a group of words with a subject and a predicate. An independent clause can stand alone. A dependent clause cannot stand alone.

Write *P* if the group of words is a phrase. Write *IC* if the group of words is an independent clause. Write *DC* if the group of words is a dependent clause.

________ with Tom and me

________ Dinesh walks

________ whenever the news comes on television

________ running and jumping in the leaves

________ around nine o'clock

________ Jaya likes drawing

________ is great at editing

________ so that he can get his work done

________ shimmering and sparkling in the sun

________ sea turtles swim many miles

________ the open bag of potato chips

________ little striped fish

________ although I knew the material

________ crashing through the woods

________ if Olive wins one more competition

________ after Rahul missed the bus

________ this pen works

________ Firoz mows the lawn

Review Work

Add uppercase letters and punctuation to the independent clauses above.

Draft Book

Use the phrases and dependent clauses to write complete sentences.

Name ______________________________

Stop the Run

independent clauses and conjunctions

When two independent clauses are written together, they create a run-on sentence. Two related independent clauses can be joined into one sentence with a comma and coordinating conjunction. There are seven coordinating conjunctions: *and*, *nor*, *but*, *for*, *yet*, *so* and *or*.

example: Jasmine needs a nap, **or** she may fall asleep.

subject predicate conjunction subject predicate

Write an *SS* above each simple subject and underline each simple predicate.

The bluebird swooped down, but it missed the grasshopper.

Vineeta read the ingredients on the ice-cream package, but she didn't find "milk" anywhere.

We are going fishing, and I am bringing my rod.

Annie gave the dog a treat, yet it is still barking.

Anita has a test tomorrow, so she is planning to study tonight.

I knitted the scarf for Sana, but she didn't like it.

Leela didn't clean her room, so she can't leave right now.

You can choose swimming for a physical education class, or you can choose gymnastics.

The phone is ringing, yet no one has answered it.

Leela's watch is under warranty, yet the store refuses to fix it.

You can clear the table, or I can do it.

Nyla and Lina love mangoes, so they are going to pick some tomorrow.

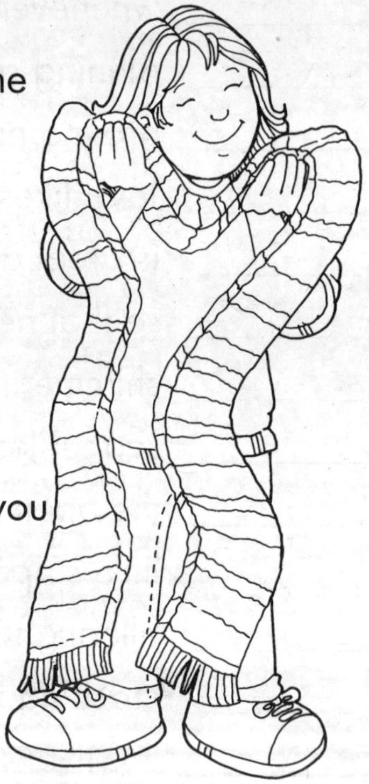

Review Work

Circle the commas and coordinating conjunctions used to separate the independent clauses.

Draft Book

Write 10 sentences that join independent clauses with commas and conjunctions.

Name ______________________________

One or Two?

independent clauses and conjunctions

When two independent clauses are written together, they create a run-on sentence. To correct a run-on, decide where the first sentence ends and the second begins. The clauses can remain in one sentence if they are separated by a comma and a coordinating conjunction. There are seven coordinating conjunctions: *and*, *nor*, *but*, *for*, *yet*, *so* and *or*.

example: The stars were coming out the moon wasn't up yet. =
The stars were coming out, but the moon wasn't up yet.

Separate each run-on sentence with a comma and a conjunction. Rewrite the sentences correctly on the lines.

Mahima was exhausted she had to finish her homework.

____

Tarun saw that man drop his wallet he returned it to him.

____

Is that box heavy is that box light?

____

The rain came down in a torrent it flooded the driveway.

____

Kartika kicked the ball hard she made the winning goal.

____

We could go to the movies we could go to the arcade.

____

I have the hiccups I am getting a glass of water.

____

Review Work

Underline the complete subjects once and the complete predicates twice.

Draft Book

Write five sentences that join independent clauses with commas and conjunctions.

Name ______________________________

Move Over a Bit

independent clauses and semicolons

When two independent clauses are written together, they create a run-on sentence. To correct a run-on, decide where the first sentence ends and the second begins. The clauses can be separated into two sentences or remain in one sentence if they are separated by a semicolon.

example: You have a cut bandage it. = You have a cut; bandage it.

Separate each run-on sentence with a semicolon. Rewrite the sentences correctly on the lines.

Walk down the hallway turn right at the end.

____

Please quit crying you are going to be fine.

____

Your alarm is ringing turn it off.

____

It could rain today take your umbrella with you.

____

Pradeep is in my class he sits right next to me.

____

The air show is in town we are going today.

____

Venus is the second planet from the Sun Earth is the third planet.

____

My nose is cold my cheeks are numb.

____

Review Work

Underline the pronouns with red.

Draft Book

Write five sentences that join independent clauses with semicolons.

Name ______________________________

Stop and Start

run-on sentences

When two independent clauses are written together, they create a run-on sentence. To correct a run-on, decide where the first sentence ends and the second begins. Separate them into two sentences by adding punctuation and uppercase letters.

example: Tarun is helpful he sets the table every night. =
Tarun is helpful. He sets the table every night.

Separate these run-on sentences. Put a punctuation mark at the end of each first sentence. Cross out the lowercase letter and write the uppercase letter above it to begin each second sentence.

The flowers are beginning to bloom I think they will need water and fertiliser.

Put the spaghetti in the water is beginning to boil.

Mia is sniffling would you get her a box of tissues?

Dad went to get groceries Aman went along.

Chitra is tie-dyeing a scarf she is being careful not to get the dye on her clothes.

Raghu bought a new puzzle it has 1,000 pieces.

Babu watched that movie he said we should see it in the theatre.

Balu earned ten rupees he will save it for our trip to the amusement park.

Julie putted the ball it dropped right into the hole.

Mahima and Aarti helped Mrs. Bal rake her yard she is a nice woman.

The squirrel jumped onto the bird feeder it scared the birds away.

Little green blueberries are on those bushes in a month they will be ready to pick.

We picked strawberries today Mom will make strawberry shortcake for dessert.

The mail carrier dropped off a big package I wonder what's in it.

Charu and Jasmine found monarch caterpillars they were on those milkweed plants.

Review Work

Underline the complete subjects once and the complete predicates twice.

Draft Book

Write 10 run-on sentences. Trade with a partner and correct each run-on sentence by separating them into complete sentences.

Name ______________________________

Breaking Apart

run-on sentences

When two independent clauses are written together, they create a run-on sentence. To correct a run-on, decide where the first sentence ends and the second begins. Separate them into two sentences by adding punctuation and uppercase letters.

example: The lion is huge he looks fierce. = The lion is huge. He looks fierce.

Separate the run-on sentences. Rewrite them correctly on the lines.

Do you know what I think I think this is fun.

____

A storm is brewing it will hit any minute.

____

Selena can't find her scissors she needs them to cut this paper.

____

Rajesh has a dog its name is Alfie.

____

The towels are in the washer they need to go into the dryer.

____

Can you see the gorilla there he is in the corner.

____

Papier-mâché is great to use the paste feels so slimy.

____

Let me see those spots oh dear, you have chicken pox!

____

Review Work

Underline the adjectives in the sentences.

Draft Book

Use one corrected sentence pair from above to write a story.

Name ________________________________

Depend On It

run-on sentences

When two independent clauses are written together, they create a run-on sentence. To correct a run-on, decide where the first sentence ends and the second begins. The clauses can be separated into two sentences or remain in one sentence if one is changed to a dependent clause. When the dependent clause is added after an independent clause, no additional punctuation is needed. When the dependent clause is added before an independent clause, a comma is placed between the two clauses.

example: I am tired I am going to bed. =
I am tired, so I am going to bed. or Since I am tired, I am going to bed.

Separate each run-on sentence. For each sentence, change one independent clause to a dependent clause. Use a variety of coordinating conjunctions. Rewrite the sentences correctly on the lines.

Mona is angry she slammed the door.

____

We can't start the movie Bijoy is not here yet.

____

It is daytime the dense clouds make it look like evening.

____

The dog walks towards her Annie smiles.

____

Mom is busy the phone rings.

____

We can go we get a ride.

____

Review Work

Underline the nouns with yellow.

Draft Book

Write 10 run-on sentences. Trade with a partner and correct each sentence by changing one clause to a dependent clause.

Name ______________________________

No More Run-Ons

run-on sentences

When two independent clauses are written together, they create a run-on sentence. To correct a run-on, decide where the first sentence ends and the second begins. The clauses can be separated into two sentences or remain in one sentence if they are separated by a comma and a conjunction or a semicolon. The clauses can also remain in one sentence if one is changed to a dependent clause.

Separate each run-on sentence. Rewrite the sentences correctly on the lines. Use each option listed above at least once.

Mohit ran to the corner Mohit walked back.

____

Jyoti fixed my computer I am grateful that she did.

____

I will bring the hose you get the sprinkler.

____

Kartika is in the chorus Priyesh is in the chorus.

____

Mr. Sridhar sharpened these scissors they work great now.

____

Tina already finished the chapter I need to finish so we can discuss it.

____

Review Work

Underline the complete subjects once and the complete predicates twice.

Draft Book

Find a page of writing in your Draft Book. Use the five options above to repair any run-on sentences.

Name ______________________________

Shorten It

abbreviations

Abbreviations of proper nouns, special titles and degrees are capatilised. Abbreviations of most common nouns are not capitalised. When used with a proper adjective, an abbreviation is capitalised. An abbreviation usually ends with a full stop.

examples: J. B. Kinard & Co.
3 Ansari Rd.

Write an abbreviation for each word. Capitalise when needed and add full stops. A few have been done for you.

drive	______	Saturday	______	Senior	______
Mister	______	ounce	______	General	______
company	______	March	______	street	______
Private	______	Saint	______	yard	yd.
Reverend	______	avenue	Ave.	Sunday	______
Doctor	______	Missus	______	inch	______
Monday	______	April	______	et cetera	______
December	______	Thursday	______	feet	______
Post Office	______	January	______	February	______
Friday	Fri.	August	______	September	______
October	______	pound	______	Junior	______
Wednesday	______	dozen	______	November	______
incorporated	______	Tuesday	______	boulevard	______
United States	______				

Review Work

Draw an X next to each proper noun.

Draft Book

Begin a list of abbreviations for future reference. Write each full word and its abbreviation.

Name ______________________________

Hey!

interjections

Interjections show strong feelings or sudden emotions. They can be words or just sounds, gasps, or exclamations that are more like noises than regular words. An interjection usually comes at the beginning of a sentence, often an exclamatory sentence. It can be followed by an exclamation mark or a comma.

Common interjections: aha, ahem, goodness, gracious, gross, grr, hello, help, hey, hooray, no, nonsense, oh, oops, ouch, phew, psst, rats, shh, super, terrific, thanks, ugh, well, wow, yes, yikes, yuck

Draw a box around each interjection and the punctuation following it.

OK, I understand this now.

Shh! We're trying to get our work done.

Ouch, get off my foot!

Wow! I passed!

Mmmm, something smells delicious!

Really, would you do that for me?

Stop! That isn't very nice.

Hold on, I'm almost finished.

Oops! I broke the lead on another pencil.

Hey, give that back!

Review Work

Write an *SS* above the simple subject in each sentence. Underline the simple predicates with blue.

Draft Book

Write 10 sentences using interjections. Write some that need commas and some that need exclamation marks.

Name ______________________________

Here and There

commas

Proper nouns name special people, places and things. When proper nouns name a city and state, a comma goes between them.

example: Madurai, Tamil Nadu

Write the addresses correctly. Apply what you know about abbreviations. Capitalise all proper nouns. Put a comma between each city and state name.

mrs seem ray ______________________________

4268/3 andheri east ______________________________

mumbai maharashtra 400099 ______________________________

dr suresh r nagarajan ______________________________

12 masilamani street ______________________________

chennai tamil nadu 600017 ______________________________

Add uppercase letters and commas where needed.

Mrs. Naidu's granddaughter lives in hyderabad andhra pradesh.

Sai got a package from bhopal madhya pradesh.

Monika ordered some clothing from mumbai maharashtra.

Rahim sent a letter from surat gujarat to patiala punjab.

Pradeep stayed overnight in madurai tamil nadu.

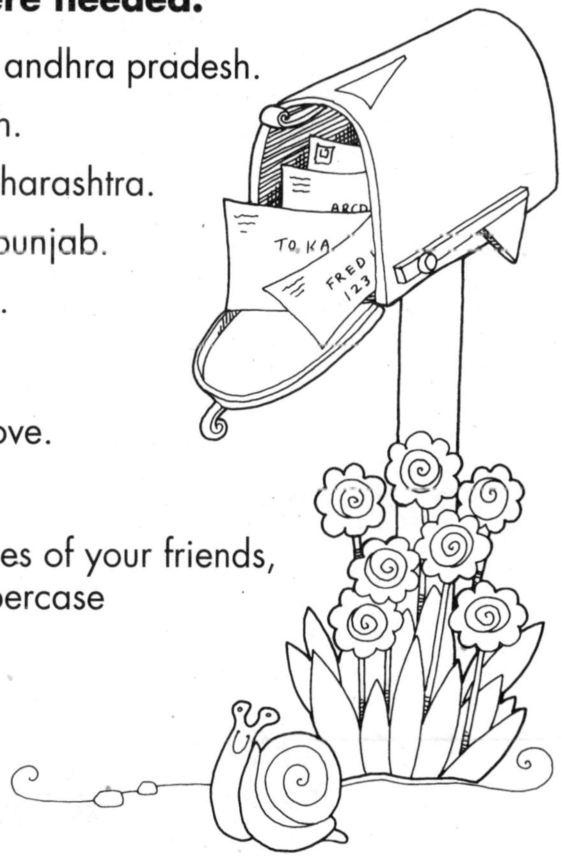

Review Work

Circle the neuter nouns in the sentences above.

Draft Book

Create an address page. Write the addresses of your friends, classmates, teachers, etc. Use commas, uppercase letters and abbreviations correctly.

Name ______________________________

Put in Your Commas

commas in dates

Commas are used in certain dates to separate the day of the week, the month and date, and the year.

yes: Saturday, March 15	no: March 15
yes: Saturday, March 15, 2003	no: March 2003
yes: March 15, 2003	

Add commas where needed in the dates.

Sunday August 18 1991 ______________________

Wednesday February 26 ______________________

October 11 1973 ______________________

December 30 ______________________

Tuesday June 29 ______________________

May 2003 ______________________

July 4 1880 ______________________

Rewrite each sentence correctly. Write out abbreviated words.

The first practice is Sat. Sept. 3.

____

Samuel's birthday is Feb. 15.

____

Sasha was born Tues. Jan. 30 2001.

____

Trishita will graduate Thurs. June 11.

____

Review Work

Choose two dates from the first section of the page. Rewrite them using abbreviations.

______________________ ______________________

Draft Book

Write 10 sentences using dates. Add commas as needed.

Name ______________________________

Reading and Viewing

titles

Underline the titles of books, magazines, newspapers, plays, movies, musicals and television shows. In typed form, these titles are often italicised instead of underlined. Quotation marks go around subsets of the above: article titles, chapter titles, essays, short stories, songs and poems. Capitalise the first and last words of a title, as well as any important words (not a preposition or article unless it is the first or last word).

Correct the titles.

Book:

walking through the waves ______________________________

Magazine or Newspaper:

the times of india ______________________________

Movie:

monsoon wedding ______________________________

Play, Musical or Opera:

bombay dreams ______________________________

Television Show:

mastermind india ______________________________

Underline the titles in the sentences.

We watch Mastermind India every Saturday night.

Raja and I went to the theatre to see Harry Potter.

Madame Butterfly is my mother's favourite opera.

Can Susie read The Hindu when you are done with it?

Kapil is in a play called Now We Are Great.

Review Work

Circle the articles with orange.

Draft Book

Look through several pages of writing in your Draft Book and check your use of titles. Make corrections where necessary.

Name ______________________________

Now Read This — quotation marks

Underline the titles of books, magazines, newspapers, plays, movies, musicals and television shows. In typed form, these titles are often italicised instead of underlined. Quotation marks go around subsets of the above: article titles, chapter titles, essays, short stories, songs and poems. Capitalise the first and last words of a title, as well as any important words (not a preposition or article unless it is the first or last word).

Correct the titles.

Chapter Title:

the broken arm ______________________________

Essay or Short Story:

how to complete your homework ______________________________

Song:

blowing in the wind ______________________________

Poem:

no means no ______________________________

Put quotation marks around the titles.

Mary memorised the poem The Tower for her presentation.

Harish handed in his essay How to Handle Little Sisters.

Since he just finished Evening in September, Nikhil now has only two chapters left.

This article called Of Course My Dog Ate It is funny.

Can Jessie read New Park Opens when you are done with the paper?

If you whistle Summer Song, the dog will howl with you.

Review Work

Circle the indefinite nouns in the sentences above.

Draft Book

Look through several pages of writing in your Draft Book and check your use of quotation marks. Make corrections where necessary.

Name ____________________

The Words Said

quotations

Direct quotations are treated in a special way. The first word of a direct quotation is capitalised. Quotation marks go around the words people say. Punctuation at the end or at a break in the quote goes inside the quotation marks.

examples: Ravi said, "This is fun."
"Stop that!" exclaimed Ravi.
"I did not hear you. What did you say?" asked Ravi.
"I like this," said Ravi.

Rewrite each sentence correctly on the line. Add quotation marks, other punctuation and uppercase letters as needed.

shekhar declared this state is a great place

____

hand washing prevents the spread of germs explained dr chandra

____

I am smarter than you retorted hari

____

can i have a peanut asked jesse

____

can't you ever quit annoying me sighed jamal

____

she exclaimed my red pen has run out of ink

____

would you like to have pizza questioned aryan

____

Review Work

Draw an X next to each proper noun that names a person.

Draft Book

Write a sentence for each verb used instead of *said*. Put quotation marks around the words people or characters say.

Name ______________________________

You Just Keep Talking

quotations

Direct quotations are treated in a special way. The first word of a direct quotation is capitalised. Quotation marks go around the words people say. Punctuation at the end or at a break in the quote goes inside the quotation marks.

examples: "Since you have prepaid tickets," stated the desk clerk, "you may enter to the right."

"This is awful," sighed Bobby. "Everything we typed was just lost."

Rewrite each sentence correctly on the line. Add quotation marks, other punctuation and uppercase letters as needed.

i really think malti insisted there is a better way

____

put your books away stated ms ray the test begins now

____

the mail capt a c hari announced has arrived

____

can't you leave me alone lucy grunted i'm busy

____

you said we could go soon persisted beena can we go now

____

i wonder questioned leela why the cat won't eat the watermelon

____

i will be on the patio explained amy reading my new book

____

Review Work

Draw an X next to each proper noun that names a person.

Draft Book

Begin a list of alternate words for *said*. Refer to this list for future writing assignments.

Name ________________________________

One Inside the Other

single quotation marks

When a word is highlighted or a title is used inside a direct quote, single quotation marks are used.

example: Sheila said, "I can't seem to spell the word 'peninsula' correctly in this paper."

At the end of a quote, the ending punctuation comes between the single and double quotation marks.

example: "Why can't I spell 'peninsula'?" asked Sheila.

Rewrite each sentence correctly. Add quotation marks, single quotation marks, other punctuation and uppercase letters as needed.

rupa said i read the article bike safety by mike b helmet

____

would you play fur elise on the piano asked gowri

____

my essay life in antarctica is due tomorrow explained ramu

____

how do you spell kangaroo questioned meera

____

we have to read nighttime maya complained it is the longest chapter

____

mom said you certainly may when i asked her replied jay

____

mr amir announced we are going to sing vande mataram

____

Review Work

Draw an X next to each proper noun that names a person. Draw a triangle next to each proper noun that names a place.

Draft Book

Add to your list of alternate words for *said*.

Name ______________________________

Dear Friend

friendly letters

Letters have five parts: date, greeting, body, closing and signature. The words in the greetings and closings begin with uppercase letters. They end with commas. Each has a line to itself.

April 5, 2002 ← date

Dear Uncle Wahid, ← greeting

I enjoyed riding horses at your farm. Cleaning the stalls was rather disgusting, but I really liked grooming your horse. I can't wait to visit you again. ← body

Love, ← closing

Wilma ← signature

Fill in the missing parts in the letter below. Include the day, month and year in the date. Label each part.

______________________ ← ______________________

Dear ______________________, ← ______________________

I went to Mrs. Menon's book reading today. It was fun. I finished a book and borrowed another. I am going back next Tuesday. I hope you can meet me there. Would you like to go to lunch before the reading? ← body

______________________ ← ______________________

______________________ ← ______________________

Review Work

Underline the nouns with yellow and the verbs with blue in the body of the letter above.

Draft Book

Write a letter to a friend. Include all of the parts listed above.

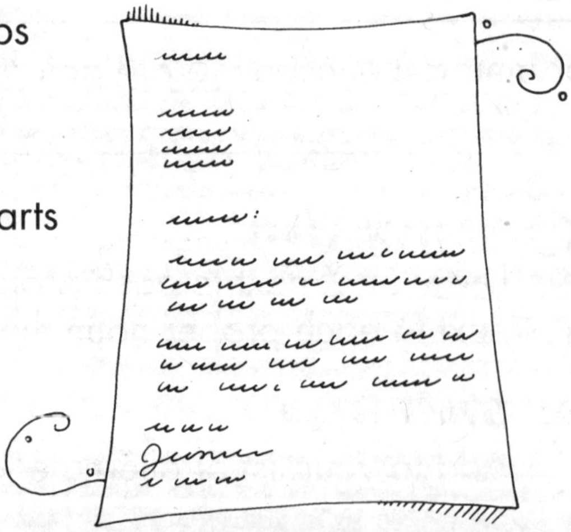

Name ______________________________

The Rules Have Changed

business letters

Business letters have seven parts: return address, date, inside address, greeting, body, closing and signature. Business letters are usually typed, all of the information is aligned on the left, and paragraphs are separated with spaces. The return address is the letter writer's address. It includes the letter writer's name, street address, city, state and pin code. The date appears directly below the return address. The inside address includes the name (and title, if necessary) of the person to whom the letter is being written, his or her company name, street address, city, state and pin code. The greeting is formal and includes the person's title and last name followed by a colon. The body follows, using the format of a personal letter. The closing is also formal; *sincerely* is an appropriate word to use. The letter ends with the letter writer's full name. Business letters should be short, formal and to the point.

Label the parts of the business letter.

mr t satish kumar
174 d n road
mumbai maharashtra 400001
saturday september 4 2004

mrs s r iyengar
chamber of commerce
190 big bazar street
coimbatore tamil nadu 641001

dear mrs s r iyengar

Hey there! I am writing this letter two request info. about
your city. mr somesh my social studies teacher said many
chamber of commerces would send info. about their towns.
I would like any materials you could send

your friend

satish

Review Work

Rewrite the letter on another sheet of paper. Make all necessary corrections.

Draft Book

Write a business letter to the Chamber of Commerce of a city you would like to visit and request information about the area and its attractions. Follow the rules for writing a business letter.

Name ______________________________

One Hundred Twenty-One — hyphens

Hyphens are used in writing. They are used between two-part numbers from twenty-one to ninety-nine when they are written as words. Hyphens are used to write fractions as words. Hyphens are also used to break a word between syllables at the end of a line.

examples: one hundred twenty-four
one-third
im-perfect, imper-fect (not imp-erfect)

Write the numbers and fractions as words.

87	____________	39	____________
43	____________	$^{1}/_{2}$	____________
781	____________	292	____________
$^{3}/_{4}$	____________	$^{9}/_{10}$	____________

Hyphenate each word for division at the end of a line. If you are unsure of syllable breaks, look in a dictionary. More than one option may be possible.

conjunction	____________	subject	____________
predicate	____________	independent	____________
dependent	____________	pronoun	____________
interjection	____________	adjective	____________
adverb	____________	preposition	____________
quotation	____________	abbreviation	____________
article	____________	appositive	____________

Review Work

Choose one of the grammar words and draw a star beside it. Write a sentence showing an example of this word.

____

Draft Book

Choose five numbers or fractions not listed above and write them as words.

Name ______________________________

No . . . or Yes? double negatives

A negative word indicates *no*. When two negative words are used, the phrase becomes a positive, or *yes*, statement. This is confusing to the reader and should be avoided. Use only one negative word when you mean to indicate *no*.

examples: We can't go nowhere. (no) We can go somewhere. (yes - positive)
We can't go anywhere. or We can go nowhere. (negative)

Write the correct negative word(s) on each line.

neither, never, no, nobody, none, no one, nor, nothing, nowhere, weren't, won't

Negative Words	Positive Opposite
______________	were
______________	somebody, anybody
______________	or
______________	either
______________	something, anything
______________	some, any
______________	will
______________	someone, anyone
______________	yes, any, a
______________	sometimes, often, ever
______________	somewhere, anywhere

Circle the correct words to make the sentences indicate no.

Jameela (will, won't) go to any practices until she is better.

I don't want (no, any) badam halwa right now.

The bananas are spoiled; we can do (nothing, something) with any of them.

The puppy (was, wasn't) nowhere to be seen.

Review Work

Underline the prepositional phrases in the sentences above.

Draft Book

Review several pages of writing in your Draft Book. Check for double negatives and make corrections where needed.

Name ____________________________

Double Trouble

double negatives

A negative word indicates *no*. When two negative words are used, the phrase becomes a positive, or *yes*, statement. This is confusing to the reader and should be avoided. Use only one negative word when you mean to indicate *no*. If a double-negative sentence contains a word like *hardly*, *barely* or *scarcely*, change the negative word to make the sentence negative.

examples: We can't go nowhere. (no) We can go somewhere. (yes - positive)
We can't hardly go anywhere. (no) or We can hardly go anywhere. (yes - positive)

Circle the negative words in each sentence. Rewrite the sentences to indicate *no*.

There is scarcely none of the birdseed left in the feeder.

____

Don't get no fries with your order. You can share mine.

____

We can't stop no one from walking in the wet grass.

____

Hardly no one ordered the pizza today.

____

There weren't no bags of popcorn left when I got there.

____

I don't have no money with me.

____

It isn't barely raining outside.

____

Review Work

Circle the adverbs with purple.

Draft Book

Write 10 sentences using double negatives. Trade with a partner and correct each sentence.

Name ______________________________

Use Two

correlative conjunctions

Correlative conjunctions are special conjunction pairs. These pairs are split by other words. There are six correlative conjunctions: *both/and*, *either/or*, *neither/nor*, *whether/or*, *just as/so*, and *not only/but also*. The correlative conjunction *neither/nor* is not a double negative.

Circle the correlative conjunctions in each sentence.

Last night both Tara and Naureen won awards.

Whether Mom drives or Dad drives, you still need to wear your seat belt.

Romila not only rode in a canoe, but also in a speedboat.

Neither Kamal nor Mira are going tonight.

Alia wanted to put some things in her scrapbook, but neither the map nor the itinerary fit.

Just as volcanoes erupt above ground, so they do deeply in the oceans.

We should see either elephants or hornbills on this trip.

Sita not only brought the cupcakes, but also made them.

Just as cars follow street signs, so must bikes.

Either a full stop or a semicolon can separate a run-on sentence.

Whether it rains or not we will play soccer.

Both the paper and the project are due on Friday.

Mr. Reddy wants to know if we can either bring a binder or send twenty rupees for a new one.

Jaya wants both caramel and fudge on her ice-cream sundae.

You not only need to wear your knee pads, but also your helmet.

Review Work

Circle the infinitives in the sentences above.

Draft Book

Write 10 sentences using correlative conjunctions from this page.

Name ________________________________

Hey, You!

direct address

A comma is used to set off the name of someone being spoken to. The comma announces to whom the speaker is talking. This is called the noun of direct address. The direct address can be added at the beginning, in the middle or at the end of the sentence.

example: Apu, I would like you to call when you get there.
I would like you to call when you get there, Apu.
I would like you to call, Apu, when you get there.

Underline the person being addressed.

Wahid, you must clean your room today.

I've been waiting for your call, Ganesh, since you left two hours ago.

Mili and Sareen went to the park, Alex.

Jan, do you know where the ruler is?

I'm going to watch the movie, Prem.

My room is clean and my homework is done, Dad.

This artwork is exceptional, Tina.

Since you have been so helpful, Daya, you can call a friend.

Tara, your story is very interesting.

Write a sentence for each situation using direct address.

Tell your dog Barkie to get off the sofa.

____

Ask your teacher when the paper is due.

____

Tell your friend to meet you in the hallway after class.

____

Review Work
Draw an X next to each proper noun that names a person.

Draft Book
Write 10 sentences using nouns of direct address.

Name ________________________________

I'm Talking to You — direct address

Commas are used to set off the name of someone being spoken to. The comma announces to whom the speaker is talking.This is called the noun of direct address. Comma placement can change the meanings of some sentences.

examples: Can I call Mom? → asking someone if you can call your mother
Can I call, Mom? → asking for permission from Mom to call someone

Write the letter in front of the sentence that gives the meaning of the sentence.

A. Stop that girl Meera.   B. Stop that girl, Meera.

_______ You are asking someone to stop a girl named Meera.

_______ You are asking Meera to stop some girl.

A. I demand another, doctor.   B. I demand another doctor.

_______ You want someone to get you a different doctor.

_______ You want the doctor to give you another of something.

A. I will ask, Preeti.   B. I will ask Preeti.

_______ You are telling Preeti you will ask someone something.

_______ You will ask Preeti something.

A. Help them push Kunal.   B. Help them push, Kunal.

_______ You are asking Kunal to help others push something.

_______ You are asking someone to help push Kunal, possibly on a sled or swing.

A. Call her Rekha.   B. Call her, Rekha.

_______ You are telling Rekha to call another girl.

_______ You are telling someone to call a girl by the name Rekha.

Review Work

Find sentences above that are not imperative sentences and draw a star next to them. Underline the subjects of the sentences with yellow.

Draft Book

Write 10 sentences using nouns of direct address.

Name ________________________________

Make it Interesting

review – sentence variety

Writing is interesting when a variety of sentence structures are used. Write one of each of the following sentence types. Examples are given to help you.

1. Write a simple subject and simple predicate.
   example: Jay walks.

   ____

2. Write a simple subject and simple predicate with adjectives, articles and/or adverbs.
   example: A tired Jay walks slowly.

   ____

3. Use an appositive.
   example: Jay, my tired little brother, walks slowly.

   ____

4. Add a direct object and possibly an indirect object.
   example: My tired little brother gives Mom a goodnight kiss.

   ____

5. Include one or more prepositions.
   example: Jay, my tired little brother, walks slowly down the hall to bed.

   ____

6. Make a compound subject and/or verb.
   example: My tired little brother kisses Mom and walks slowly to bed.

   ____

7. Use a dependent clause.
   example: When the moon came out, Jay, my little brother, kissed Mom and walked to bed.

   ____

8. Join independent clauses.
   example: My little brother kisses Mom, and he walks down the hall to bed.

   ____

9. Add conversation.
   example: "Goodnight," whispered Jay as he kissed Mom and walked to bed.

   ____

Name ________________________________

Rocks

review

This is the piece you began with at the beginning of your grammar study. Use it to demonstrate your improved understanding of grammar. Follow the directions on this page and page 114.

(1)Arun studies rocks and minerals with his class. (2)The class observes rocks, performs field tests on the minerals and reads extensively about both. (3)He discovered that there are three types of rocks: sedimentary, igneous and metamorphic.

(4)Sedimentary rocks are formed in layers. (5)The layers are deposited in streams and riverbeds. (6)Sand, pebbles, plant matter and animal parts can all end up in these layers. (7)Over time, the layers solidify, and sedimentary rock is formed. (8)The plant matter and animal parts become fossils.

(9)Igneous rocks are formed in, under and around volcanoes. (10)The molten rock, or heated liquid rock, forms underground. (11)It is called magma. (12)Some magma cools slowly underground, becoming igneous rock. (13)Pressure causes other magma to rise to the surface. (14)When magma exits the volcano, its name changes to lava. (16)Lava flows from the volcano, incinerating everything it touches. (17)Finally, it cools. (18)Solidified lava is igneous rock. (19)Igneous rocks have many different looks depending on how quickly they cool. (20)Igneous rock can have air bubbles and be very light, or it can be jet black and very solid.

(21)Metamorphic rock is changed rock. (22)It forms deep underground. (23)Sedimentary or igneous rock that has been compressed by underground pressure and heat becomes metamorphic rock. (24)The heat and pressure cause the layers of sedimentary and igneous rock to become meshed together, much like the cheese in a grilled-cheese sandwich meshes slightly with the bread on each side.

(25)These three rock types are the literal building blocks of Earth. (26)They provide stability to our structures and provide many building materials for the items we use daily. (27)Arun finds rocks fascinating.

Rewrite sentence number 27 to include a quotation.

____

Circle the tense this article is written in:

present tense   past tense   future tense

Write the sentence number.

Find two independent clauses joined by a comma and a conjunction. __________

Find an independent clause that precedes a dependent clause and is joined by a comma. __________

Find a sentence that begins with a dependent clause. __________

Look at sentence number 1. Write an *SS* above the simple subject and underline the simple predicate.

Name ______________________________

Rocks (cont.)

review

Look at sentence number 11. Underline the complete subject once and the complete predicate twice.

Find and write an example from the passage on the line. Write the sentence number behind it.

article ______________________________

proper noun ______________________________

common noun ______________________________

subject pronoun ______________________________

possessive pronoun ______________________________

indefinite, or neutral, noun ______________________________

compound subject ______________________________

action verb ______________________________

common adjective ______________________________

demonstrative adjective ______________________________

adverb ______________________________

helping verb ______________________________

linking verb + predicate noun ______________________________

infinitive ______________________________

direct object ______________________________

object of the preposition ______________________________

appositive ______________________________

On a separate piece of paper, write a business letter to Ms. Jade Opal requesting information about joining the Rock and Mineral Club.

Name ______________________________

Student Editing Checklist

Check each highlighted item*

- [ ] Each sentence has a complete subject and a complete predicate.
- [ ] Run-on sentences are avoided.
- [ ] Sentence variety is used.
- [ ] Phrases and dependent clauses are not used as sentences.
- [ ] Subjects agree with verbs and pronouns.
- [ ] Double negatives are corrected.
- [ ] The first letter in each sentence is capitalised, including the first letter inside quotation marks.
- [ ] The pronoun I is always capitalised.
- [ ] Each word that names a day, month or holiday starts with an uppercase letter.
- [ ] Each proper noun starts with an uppercase letter.
- [ ] Each title starts with an uppercase letter.
- [ ] Quotations follow correct format for punctuation and capitalisation.
- [ ] Friendly and business letters follow correct format.
- [ ] Each declarative sentence ends with a full stop.
- [ ] Each imperative sentence ends with a full stop or exclamation mark.
- [ ] Each interrogative sentence ends with a question mark.
- [ ] Each exclamatory sentence ends with an exclamation mark.
- [ ] Commas are used to separate dates.
- [ ] Commas are used in the greeting and closing in a friendly letter.
- [ ] A comma is used between a city and state.
- [ ] A dependent clause that precedes an independent clause is followed by a comma.
- [ ] Two independent clauses are joined with a conjunction and a comma.
- [ ] Abbreviations end with full stops.
- [ ] Quotation marks are used around direct quotations, and certain titles.
- [ ] Book titles are underlined.

* Teacher highlights items for individual student editing.

Name ______________________________

Student Editing Checklist

- ☐ Hyphens are used in numbers, fractions and syllables at the ends of lines.
- ☐ A plural noun usually ends in *s* or *es*.
- ☐ A possessive noun usually ends in *'s*.
- ☐ Subject pronouns come before verbs.
- ☐ Object pronouns come after verbs.
- ☐ Possessive pronouns take the place of possessive nouns.
- ☐ Indefinite pronouns refer to nouns in a general way.
- ☐ Intensive pronouns draw attention to nouns or pronouns.
- ☐ Reflexive pronouns reflect back to the subjects of sentences.
- ☐ All verb tenses correctly describe when something is happening.
- ☐ Singular verbs follow singular nouns.
- ☐ Plural verbs follow plural nouns.
- ☐ Words are spelt correctly for their meanings.
- ☐ Articles are used before nouns or adjective/noun combinations.
- ☐ Apostrophes take the place of dropped letters in contractions.
- ☐ Other: ____

* Teacher highlights items for individual student editing.

Answer Key

Page 6

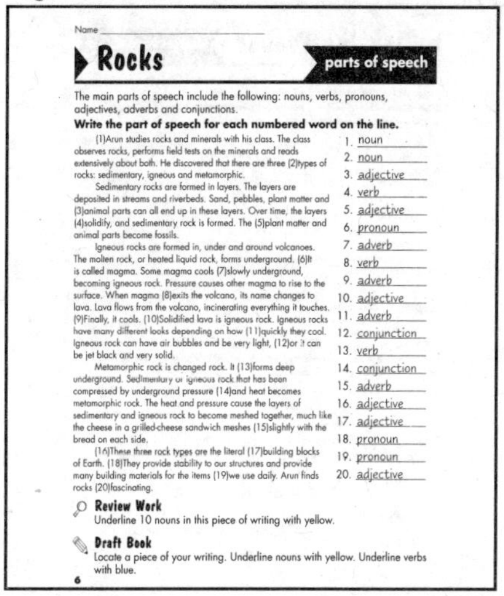

RW: Answers will vary. DB: Answers will vary.

Page 7

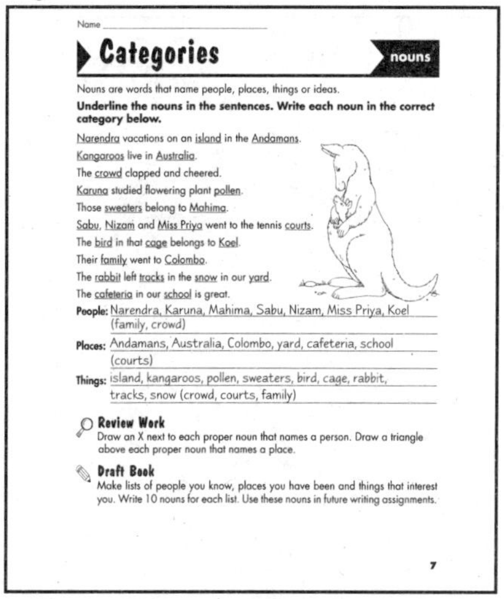

RW: Draw an X next to Narendra, Karuna, Mahima, Sabu, Nizam, Miss Priya and Koel. Draw a triangle above Andamans, Australia and Colombo. DB: Answers will vary.

Page 8

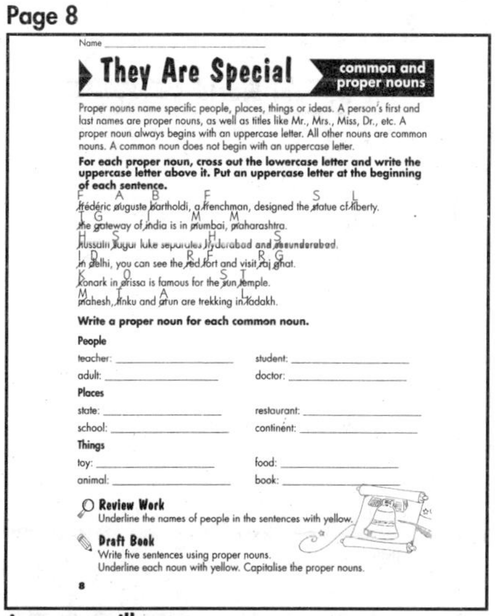

Answers will vary.
RW: Underline Frédéric Auguste Bartholdi, Mahesh, Tinku and Arun with yellow.
DB: Answers will vary.

Page 9

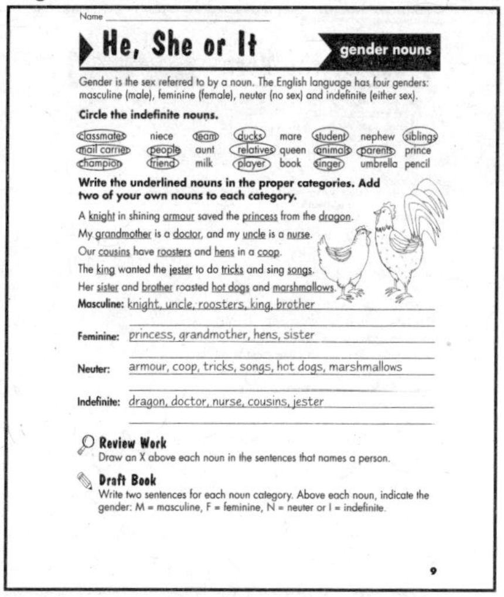

RW: Draw an X above knight, princess, grandmother, doctor, uncle, nurse, cousins, king, jester, sister and brother.
DB: Answers will vary.

Page 10

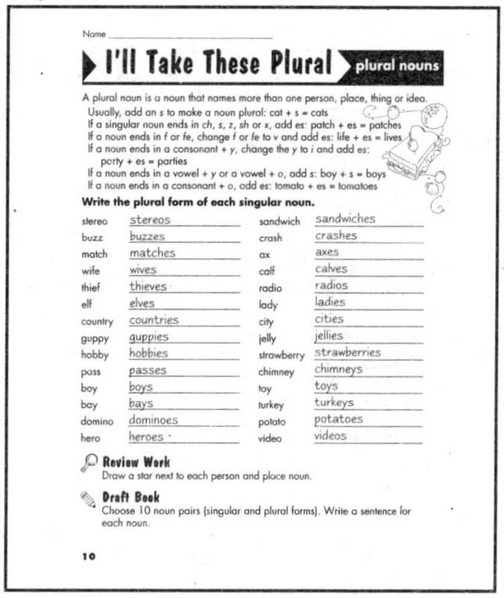

RW: Draw a star next to wives, thieves, countries, boys, bays, heroes, ladies and cities. DB: Answers will vary.

Page 11

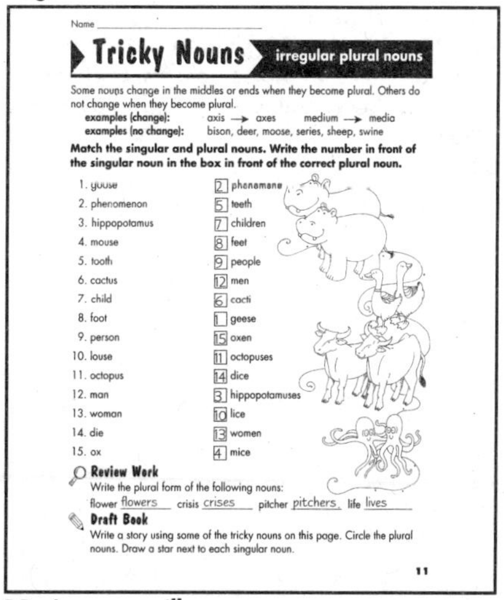

DB: Answers will vary.

Page 12

RW: Underline snails, colours, teachers, crayons, dancers, children and balloons with yellow.
DB: Answers will vary.

Page 13

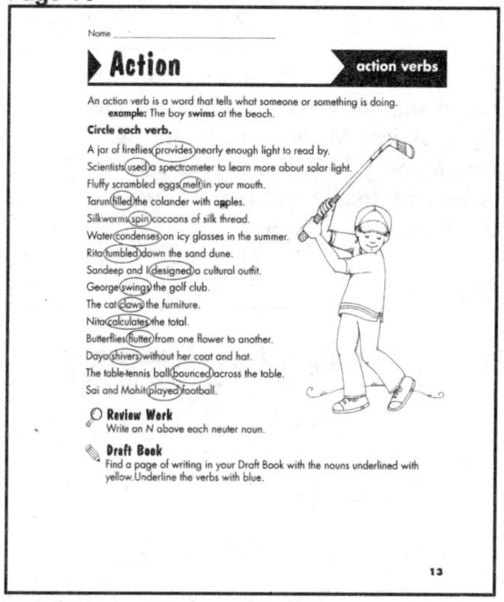

RW: Write an N above jar, light, spectrometer, light, eggs, mouth, colander, apples, cocoons, thread, water, glasses, summer, dune, outfit, club, furniture, total, flower, coat, hat, ball, table and football. DB: Answers will vary.

Page 14

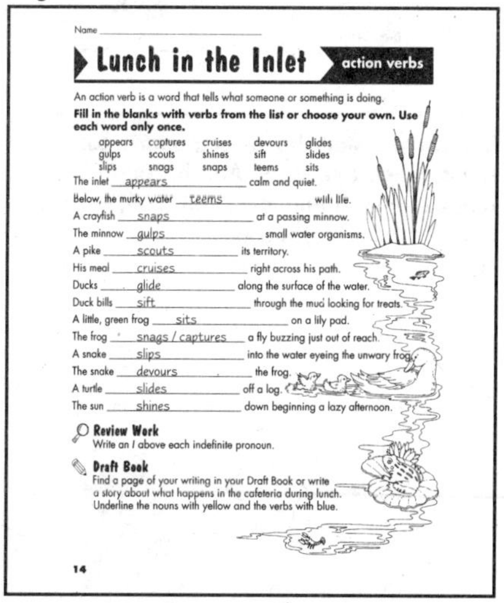

Answer Key

Page 14 (cont.)
RW: Write I above crayfish, minnow, minnow, organisms, pike, ducks, frog, frog, fly, snake, frog, snake and turtle.
DB: Answers will vary.

Page 15

Name

Give a Helping Hand helping verbs/ verb phrases

Helping verbs are verbs that help main verbs express tense. There are 23 helping verbs. A verb phrase acts as a single verb and is made of a main verb with one or more helping verbs. Up to three helping verbs can precede the main verb. Would, should, shall and will are helping verbs. Forms of the following verbs are also helping verbs:

be: am, are, is, was, were, be, being, been
do: do, does, did
have: have, has, had
may: may, must, might
can: can, could

Circle the helping verbs. Underline the verb phrases.

The fleas did jump through the cat's fur.
The water is pouring into the basement.
The ant had scurried into the anthill.
We are going to the amusement park.
I am excited to be here.
The lights can be dimmed with this switch.
Mudit was entitled to his turn.
The puppy must have tried to jump onto the bed.
That jam would make a good ice-cream topping.
The bird had flown into the bushes.
We should weed the garden before it gets too hot.
The tickets may cost too much.
Sabeena's family might go to the zoo tomorrow.

Review Work
Underline the nouns with yellow.

Draft Book
Write 10 sentences that use helping verbs. Circle the helping verbs. Underline the verb phrases with blue.

15

RW: RW: Underline fleas, cat's, fur, water, basement, ant, anthill, amusement park, lights, switch, Mudit, turn, puppy, bed, jam, topping, bird, bushes, garden, tickets, Sabeena's, family and zoo with yellow.
DB: Answers will vary.

Page 16

Name

Link Them Together linking verbs

A linking verb is a verb that does not show action. It links or joins something in the predicate to the rest of the sentence. It does not have an action verb after it. Forms of the verb to be are the most common linking verbs. There are eight forms of the verb to be: am, are, is, was, were, (will) be, (am, are, was, were) being, (have, has, had) been. Other linking verbs include forms of these verbs: to appear, to become, to feel, to grow, to look, to remain, to seem, to smell, to sound and to taste.

Underline the linking verbs.

The knitted sweaters are very warm.
The food on the table appears appetising.
The neighbour's dog, who was sprayed by a skunk, smells awful.
The garbage can by the door is full.
That frozen drink tastes fruity.
The lilac bushes, planted when I was born, grow more beautiful every year.
Lata, Apu's big sister, is our junior counsellor.
Anush, my younger cousin, will be in first grade next year.
The moon was like a huge orange ball hovering in the sky.
The music, which played for hours, grew increasingly louder.
Ms. Tania, my mom's friend, is a pediatric neurosurgeon.
Mom's new scissors are sharp enough to cut corrugated cardboard.
Mr. Suresh, my orthodontist, is nice.
Last night Venus was visible low in the sky.

Review Work
Draw a star above each person noun.

Draft Book
Write 10 sentences that use linking verbs. Use a variety of the linking verbs listed above. Underline the linking verbs with blue.

16

RW: Draw a star above neighbour's, Lata, Apu's, sister, counsellor, Anush, cousin, Ms. Tania, mom's, friend, neurosurgeon, Mom's, Mr. Suresh and orthodontist.
DB: Answers will vary.

Page 17

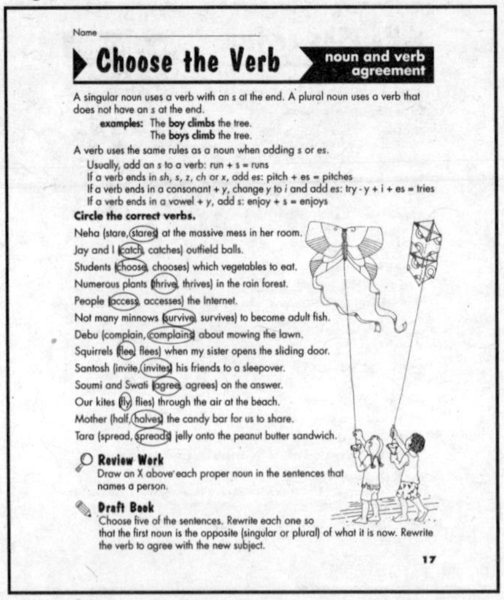
Name

Choose the Verb noun and verb agreement

A singular noun uses a verb with an s at the end. A plural noun uses a verb that does not have an s at the end.
examples: The boy climbs the tree.
The boys climb the tree.

A verb uses the same rules as a noun when adding s or es.
Usually, add an s to a verb: run + s = runs
If a verb ends in sh, s, z, ch or x, add es: pitch + es = pitches
If a verb ends in a consonant + y, change y to i and add es: try - y + i + es = tries
If a verb ends in a vowel + y, add s: enjoy + s = enjoys

Circle the correct verbs.

Neha (stare, stares) at the massive mess in her room.
Jay and I (catch, catches) outfield balls.
Students (choose, chooses) which vegetables to eat.
Numerous plants (thrive, thrives) in the rain forest.
People (access, accesses) the Internet.
Not many minnows (survive, survives) to become adult fish.
Debu (complain, complains) about mowing the lawn.
Squirrels (flee, flees) when my sister opens the sliding door.
Santosh (invite, invites) his friends to a sleepover.
Soumi and Swati (agree, agrees) on the answer.
Our kites (fly, flies) through the air at the beach.
Mother (half, halves) the candy bar for us to share.
Tara (spread, spreads) jelly onto the peanut butter sandwich.

Review Work
Draw an X above each proper noun in the sentences that names a person.

Draft Book
Choose five of the sentences. Rewrite each one so that the first noun is the opposite (singular or plural) of what it is now. Rewrite the verb to agree with the new subject.

17

RW: Draw an X above Neha, Jay, Debu, Santosh, Soumi, Swati, Mother and Tara.
DB: Answers will vary.

Page 18

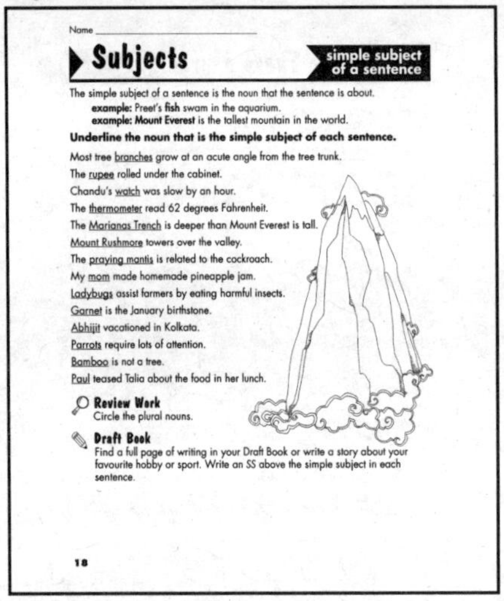
Name

Subjects simple subject of a sentence

The simple subject of a sentence is the noun that the sentence is about.
example: Preet's fish swam in the aquarium.
example: Mount Everest is the tallest mountain in the world.

Underline the noun that is the simple subject of each sentence.

Most tree branches grow at an acute angle from the tree trunk.
The rupee rolled under the cabinet.
Chandu's watch was slow by an hour.
The thermometer read 62 degrees Fahrenheit.
The Marianas Trench is deeper than Mount Everest is tall.
Mount Rushmore towers over the valley.
The praying mantis is related to the cockroach.
My mom made homemade pineapple jam.
Ladybugs assist farmers by eating harmful insects.
Garnet is the January birthstone.
Abhijit vacationed in Kolkata.
Parrots require lots of attention.
Bamboo is not a tree.
Paul teased Talia about the food in her lunch.

Review Work
Circle the plural nouns.

Draft Book
Find a full page of writing in your Draft Book or write a story about your favourite hobby or sport. Write an SS above the simple subject in each sentence.

18

RW: Circle branches, degrees, ladybugs, insects and parrots.
DB: Answers will vary.

Page 19:
Answers will vary.
RW: Underline drawing, ingredient, meal, trees, table, homes, flower, places, backyard, everything, task, plants, park and snack with yellow.
DB: Answers will vary.

Page 20

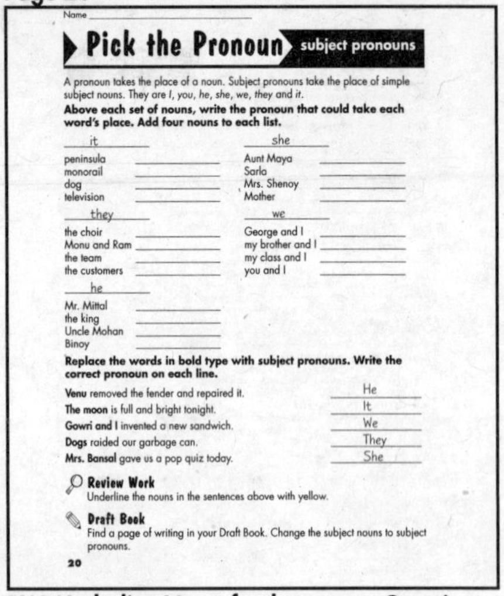
Name

Pick the Pronoun subject pronouns

A pronoun takes the place of a noun. Subject pronouns take the place of simple subject nouns. They are I, you, he, she, we, they and it.

Above each set of nouns, write the pronoun that could take each word's place. Add four nouns to each list.

it: peninsula, monorail, dog, television
she: Aunt Maya, Sarla, Mrs. Shenoy, Mother
they: the choir, Monu and Ram, the team, the customers
we: George and I, my brother and I, my class and I, you and I
he: Mr. Mittal, the king, Uncle Mohan, Binoy

Replace the words in bold type with subject pronouns. Write the correct pronoun on each line.

Venu removed the fender and repaired it. — He
The moon is full and bright tonight. — It
Gowri and I invented a new sandwich. — We
Dogs raided our garbage can. — They
Mrs. Bansal gave us a pop quiz today. — She

Review Work
Underline the nouns in the sentences above with yellow.

Draft Book
Find a page of writing in your Draft Book. Change the subject nouns to subject pronouns.

20

RW: Underline Venu, fender, moon, Gowri, sandwich, dogs, can, Mrs. Bansal and pop quiz with yellow.

Page 21

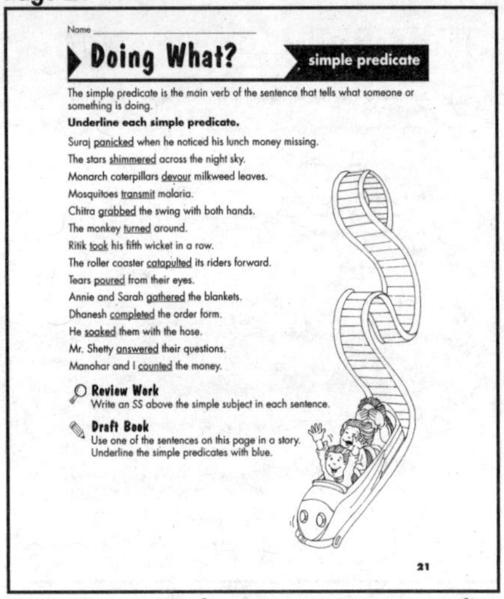
Name

Doing What? simple predicate

The simple predicate is the main verb of the sentence that tells what someone or something is doing.

Underline each simple predicate.

Suraj panicked when he noticed his lunch money missing.
The stars shimmered across the night sky.
Monarch caterpillars devour milkweed leaves.
Mosquitoes transmit malaria.
Chitra grabbed the swing with both hands.
The monkey turned around.
Ritik took his fifth wicket in a row.
The roller coaster catapulted its riders forward.
Tears poured from their eyes.
Annie and Sarah gathered the blankets.
Dhanesh completed the order form.
He soaked them with the hose.
Mr. Shetty answered their questions.
Manohar and I counted the money.

Review Work
Write an SS above the simple subject in each sentence.

Draft Book
Use one of the sentences on this page in a story. Underline the simple predicates with blue.

21

RW: Write an SS above Suraj, stars, caterpillars, mosquitoes, Chitra, monkey, Ritik, roller coaster, tears, Annie, Sarah, Dhanesh, he, Mr. Shetty, Manohar and I.
DB: Answers will vary.

Page 22

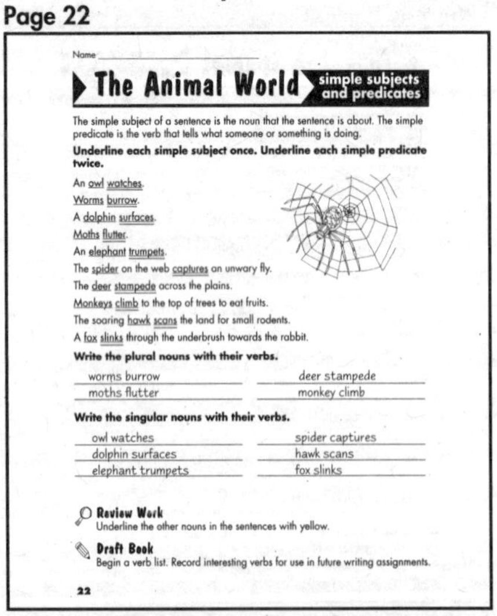
Name

The Animal World simple subjects and predicates

The simple subject of a sentence is the noun that the sentence is about. The simple predicate is the verb that tells what someone or something is doing.

Underline each simple subject once. Underline each simple predicate twice.

An owl watches.
Worms burrow.
A dolphin surfaces.
Moths flutter.
An elephant trumpets.
The spider on the web captures an unwary fly.
The deer stampede across the plains.
Monkeys climb to the top of trees to eat fruits.
The soaring hawk scans the land for small rodents.
A fox slinks through the underbrush towards the rabbit.

Write the plural nouns with their verbs.

worms burrow — deer stampede
moths flutter — monkey climb

Write the singular nouns with their verbs.

owl watches — spider captures
dolphin surfaces — hawk scans
elephant trumpets — fox slinks

Review Work
Underline the other nouns in the sentences with yellow.

Draft Book
Begin a verb list. Record interesting verbs for use in future writing assignments.

22

RW: Underline web, fly, plains, trees, fruits, land, rodents, underbrush and rabbit with yellow. DB: Answers will vary.

Answer Key

Page 23

Name

It Happened Before — past tense

Tense tells time. It informs the reader when the sentence takes place. If the action happened in the past, it is past tense. There are several ways to make a verb past tense.

Usually, add ed or d to a verb: box + ed = boxed, wave + d = waved.

If a verb ends with a consonant + y, change y to i and add ed: carry - y + i + ed = carried.

If a verb has a short vowel with one consonant, double the consonant then add ed: tip + p + ed = tipped, stop + p + ed = stopped.

Use the rules above to make the verbs past tense.

rustle	rustled	end	ended
bat	batted	cry	cried
splatter	splattered	trip	tripped
agree	agreed	snap	snapped
ship	shipped	create	created

Write the correct past tense verb on each line.

Satish (copy) copied his work onto clean paper.
The kitten (pounce) pounced on the ladybug.
Smrti (try) tried spinach for the first time.
The firefighter (parachute) parachuted into the fire zone.
Raju (hurry) hurried to his piano lesson.
Aparna (play) played with her cousin.
Zuhoor (shop) shopped for new shoes.

Review Work Write an SS above the simple subject in each sentence.

Draft Book Choose five verb pairs (present and past tense). Write two sentences for each verb. Use the present tense verb in one sentence and the past tense verb in the other.

23

RW: Write an SS above Satish, kitten, Smrti, firefighter, Raju, Aparna and Zuhoor.
DB: Answers will vary.

Page 24

Name

Now or Then — past and present tense

Tense tells time. When it happened in the past, it is past tense. When something happens now, it is present tense.

Underline the verb in each first sentence. Write the past tense of the verb in each second sentence.

Children crawl through the obstacle course.
Yesterday, they crawled through by the hundreds.
Mosquitoes bother the horses.
They bothered the dogs last week.
Collin bounces on the trampoline.
He bounced on it with Anand earlier.
Chitra and I roll the chapati dough very carefully.
We rolled enough dough to make six dozen chapatis.
The doctor inoculates the child.
She inoculated several children this morning.
Tara and Nilesh drift along on the inner tubes.
They drifted downstream.
The news helicopter hovers over the scene.
It hovered there until the photos were taken.
Mahesh tastes the broccoli salad.
He tasted the chutney earlier.

Review Work Underline the subject nouns in the first sentences with yellow. Underline the pronouns that replaced them in the second sentences with red.

Draft Book Find a story you wrote in your Draft Book. Put boxes around verbs with ed endings.

24

RW: Underline children, mosquitoes, Collin, Chitra and I, doctor, Tara and Nilesh, helicopter and Mahesh with yellow.
Underline they, they, he, we, she, they, it and he with red. DB: Answers will vary.

Page 25

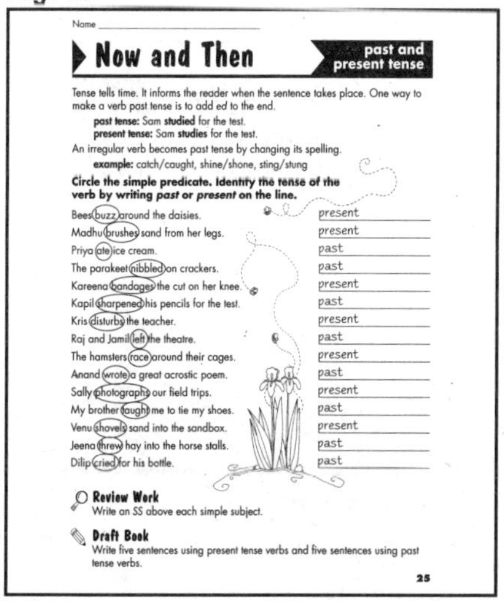

Name

Now and Then — past and present tense

Tense tells time. It informs the reader when the sentence takes place. One way to make a verb past tense is to add ed to the end.

past tense: Sam studied for the test.
present tense: Sam studies for the test.

An irregular verb becomes past tense by changing its spelling.
example: catch/caught, shine/shone, sting/stung

Circle the simple predicate. Identify the tense of the verb by writing *past* or *present* on the line.

Bees buzz around the daisies. — present
Madhu brushes sand from her legs. — present
Priya ate ice cream. — past
The parakeet nibbled on crackers. — past
Kareena bandages the cut on her knee. — present
Kapil sharpened his pencils for the test. — past
Kris disturbs the teacher. — present
Raj and Jamil left the theatre. — past
The hamsters race around their cages. — present
Anand wrote a great acrostic poem. — past
Sally photographs our field trips. — present
My brother taught me to tie my shoes. — past
Venu shovels sand into the sandbox. — present
Jeena threw hay into the horse stalls. — past
Dilip cried for his bottle. — past

Review Work Write an SS above each simple subject.

Draft Book Write five sentences using present tense verbs and five sentences using past tense verbs.

25

Page 25 (cont.)

RW: Write an SS above bees, Madhu, Priya, parakeet, Kareena, Kapil, Kris, Raj, Jamil, hamsters, Anand, Sally, brother, Venu, Jeena and Dilip.
DB: Answers will vary.

Page 26

Name

Things to Come — future tense

Tense tells time. It informs the reader when the sentence takes place. To make a verb future tense, add the helping verb will before the singular present tense form of the verb. If the verb has an ending, drop it before adding will.

example: Babu rakes the lawn. Babu will rake the lawn. Jon ate the apple. Jon will eat the apple.

Write the correct future tense verb on each line.

Jairam (builds) will build a birdhouse.
Ali (caught) will catch some fish.
The boat (cruises) will cruise around the channel.
Balu and Raghu (jumped) will jump into the pool.
The class (observes) will observe the plants as they grow.
Jay (painted) will paint that set of chairs.
The monkey (grabbed) will grab the rope.
Kunal (helped) will help make the cake.
Charu (completed) will complete the book.
A dolphin (bumps) will bump the boat gently.
Jyoti (brought) will bring cupcakes for the party.
The sauce (burns) will burn with the burner on high.
Diya (carries) will carry the pineapples to the car.
Ayan, Manoj and Jacob (threw) will throw water balloons.
The silverware (clatters) will clatter to the floor.

Review Work Underline the nouns with yellow.

Draft Book Write about an imaginary trip using future tense verbs.

26

RW: Underline Jairam, birdhouse, Ali, fish, boat, channel, Balu, Raghu, pool, class, plants, Jay, set, chairs, monkey, rope, Kunal, cake, Charu, book, dolphin, boat, Jyoti, cupcakes, party, sauce, burner, Diya, pineapples, car, Ayan, Manoj, Jacob, balloons, silverware and floor with yellow.
DB: Answers will vary.

Page 27

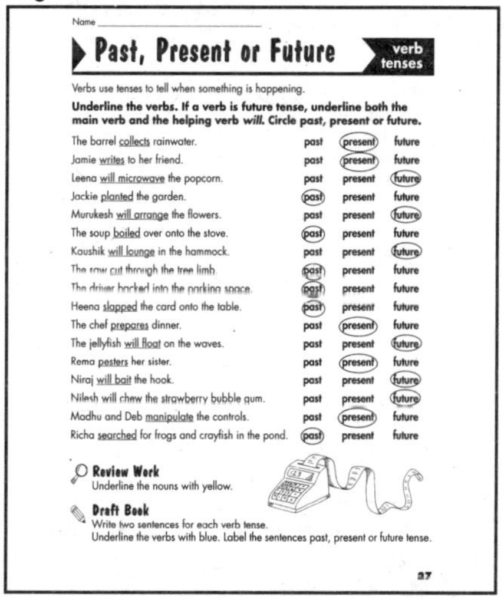

Name

Past, Present or Future — verb tenses

Verbs use tenses to tell when something is happening.

Underline the verbs. If a verb is future tense, underline both the main verb and the helping verb *will*. Circle past, present or future.

Sentence	Answer
The barrel collects rainwater.	present
Jamie writes to her friend.	present
Leena will microwave the popcorn.	future
Jackie planted the garden.	past
Murukesh will arrange the flowers.	future
The soup boiled over onto the stove.	past
Koushik will lounge in the hammock.	future
The saw cut through the tree limb.	past
The driver backed into the parking space.	past
Heena slapped the card onto the table.	past
The chef prepares dinner.	present
The jellyfish will float on the waves.	future
Rema pesters her sister.	present
Niraj will bait the hook.	future
Nilesh will chew the strawberry bubble gum.	future
Madhu and Deb manipulate the controls.	present
Richa searched for frogs and crayfish in the pond.	past

Review Work Underline the nouns with yellow.

Draft Book Write two sentences for each verb tense. Underline the verbs with blue. Label the sentences past, present or future tense.

27

RW: Underline barrel, rainwater, Jamie, friend, Leena, popcorn, Jackie, garden, Murukesh, flowers, soup, stove, Kaushik, hammock, saw, limb, driver, space, Heena, card, table, chef, dinner, jellyfish, waves, Rema, sister, Niraj, hook, Nilesh, bubble gum, Madhu, Deb, controls, Richa, frogs, crayfish and pond with yellow.
DB: Answers will vary.

Page 28

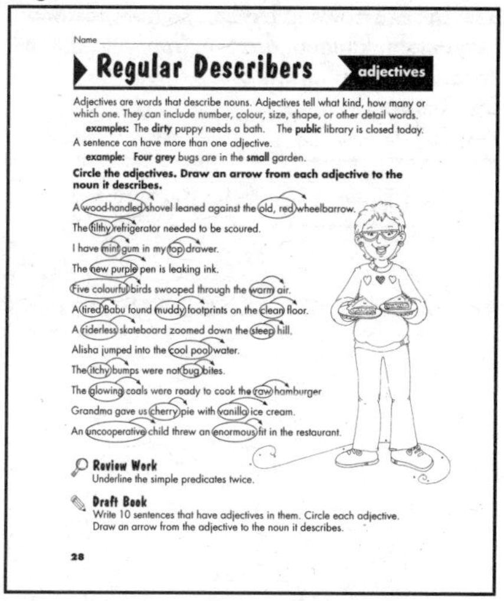

Name

Regular Describers — adjectives

Adjectives are words that describe nouns. Adjectives tell what kind, how many or which one. They can include number, colour, size, shape, or other detail words.

examples: The dirty puppy needs a bath. The public library is closed today.

A sentence can have more than one adjective.

example: Four grey bugs are in the small garden.

Circle the adjectives. Draw an arrow from each adjective to the noun it describes.

A wood-handled shovel leaned against the old, red wheelbarrow.
The filthy refrigerator needed to be scoured.
I have mint gum in my top drawer.
The new purple pen is leaking ink.
Five colourful birds swooped through the warm air.
A tired Babu found muddy footprints on the clean floor.
A riderless skateboard zoomed down the steep hill.
Alisha jumped into the cool pool water.
The itchy bumps were not bug bites.
The glowing coals were ready to cook the raw hamburger.
Grandma gave us cherry pie with vanilla ice cream.
An uncooperative child threw an enormous fit in the restaurant.

Review Work Underline the simple predicates twice.

Draft Book Write 10 sentences that have adjectives in them. Circle each adjective. Draw an arrow from the adjective to the noun it describes.

28

RW: Underline leaned, needed, have, is, swooped, found, zoomed, jumped, were, were, gave and threw twice.
DB: Answers will vary.

Page 29

Name

Other Describers — demonstrative and common adjectives

Adjectives are words that describe nouns. Adjectives tell what kind, how many or which one. They can include number, colour, size, shape or other detail words. The four demonstrative adjectives that answer which one are: this, that, these and those. Common adjectives are regular adjectives.

Circle the adjectives. Draw an arrow from each adjective to the noun it describes.

Those scented candles produce very hot wax.
That four-year-old child chatters constantly.
This fuzzy peach has a bruised spot.
Those majestic glaciers tower above this cruise ship.
That dirty blue sock has a small hole in the toe.
This yellow pencil has a broken point.
My little sister is in that class.
Vineet wants that chocolate cupcake with white frosting.
Veena drew that seaside sketch with the thunderous storm clouds.
These tiny black seeds can grow delicious white radishes.
Those glass marbles belong to that boy.
That black camera takes great photographs.

Review Work Write a D above each demonstrative adjective.

Draft Book Write 10 sentences that have adjectives in them. Circle each adjective. Draw an arrow from the adjective to the noun it describes.

29

RW: Write a D above those, that, this, those, this, that, this, that, that, that, these, those, that and that. DB: Answers will vary.

Page 30

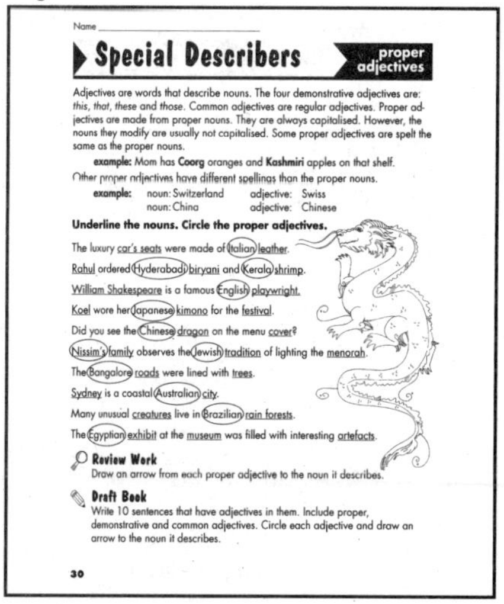

Name

Special Describers — proper adjectives

Adjectives are words that describe nouns. The four demonstrative adjectives are: this, that, these and those. Common adjectives are regular adjectives. Proper adjectives are made from proper nouns. They are always capitalised. However, the nouns they modify are usually not capitalised. Some proper adjectives are spelt the same as the proper nouns.

example: Mom has Coorg oranges and Kashmiri apples on that shelf.

Other proper adjectives have different spellings than the proper nouns.

example: noun: Switzerland — adjective: Swiss; noun: China — adjective: Chinese

Underline the nouns. Circle the proper adjectives.

The luxury car's seats were made of Italian leather.
Rahul ordered Hyderabadi biryani and Kerala shrimp.
William Shakespeare is a famous English playwright.
Koel wore her Japanese kimono for the festival.
Did you see the Chinese dragon on the menu cover?
Nissim's family observes the Jewish tradition of lighting the menorah.
The Bangalore roads were lined with trees.
Sydney is a coastal Australian city.
Many unusual creatures live in Brazilian rain forests.
The Egyptian exhibit at the museum was filled with interesting artefacts.

Review Work Draw an arrow from each proper adjective to the noun it describes.

Draft Book Write 10 sentences that have adjectives in them. Include proper, demonstrative and common adjectives. Circle each adjective and draw an arrow to the noun it describes.

30

Answer Key

Page 30 (cont.)

RW: Draw arrows to leather, biriyani, shrimp, playwright, kimono, dragon, family, tradition, roads, city, rain forests and exhibit.

DB: Answers will vary.

Page 31

Name ______________

Choose Your Adjective — adjectives

Adjectives are words that describe nouns. The four demonstrative adjectives are: *this, that, these* and *those*. Common adjectives, like common nouns, are not capitalised. Proper adjectives are made from proper nouns. They are always capitalised. However, the nouns they modify are not usually capitalised.

Underline the nouns. Circle the proper adjectives. Draw an arrow from each proper adjective to the noun it describes.

That Agra petha is absolutely delicious.

Sunita studied about Roman emperors for her social studies test.

The Arctic region is home to little, white, baby harp seals.

Abu made an acute angle on that triangle.

We are eating Gujarati food for dinner tonight.

Those noisy birds woke up the entire neighbourhood.

Neena went to a Chennai zoo to see the cute Nilgiri Tahrs.

Sohan parked his green mountain bike next to that chain-link fence.

The best hunters around are the Bengal tigers.

My grandmother has Hyderabadi pearls in her jewel case.

My Pakistani relatives hosted an Iftar party this year.

Review Work
Write a *D* above each demonstrative adjective.

Draft Book
Write 10 sentences that have adjectives in them. Include proper, demonstrative and common adjectives. Circle each adjective. Draw an arrow from the adjective to the noun it describes.

31

RW: Write a D above that, that, those, that and this. DB: Answers will vary.

Page 32

Name ______________

At the End — adjectives: positive, comparative, superlative

Adjectives describe and/or compare nouns. There are three degrees of comparison. The positive degree describes a noun (or nouns). The comparative degree compares two nouns (add *er* or the words *more* or *less*). The superlative degree compares more than two nouns (add *est* or the words *most* or *least*).

Usually, comparative and superlative adjectives are formed by adding the suffixes er and est with no changes to the base words. There are some exceptions.

If an adjective ends with e, drop the *e* and add *er* or *est*: rare + est = rarest.
If an adjective ends in a consonant + *y*, change *y* to *i* and add *er* or *est*: funny - y + er = funnier.
If an adjective has a short vowel with one consonant, double the consonant then add *er* or *est*: mad + d + er = madder.
If an adjective has two or more syllables, use *more, most, less* or *least* in front of it.

Add *er* and *est* to each adjective to make the comparative and superlative forms.

Positive	Comparative	Superlative
angry	angrier	angriest
wise	wiser	wisest
fast	faster	fastest
great	greater	greatest

Add *more* and *most* to each adjective to make the comparative and superlative forms.

Positive	Comparative	Superlative
delicious	more delicious	most delicious
interesting	more interesting	most interesting
vibrant	more vibrant	most vibrant
majestic	more majestic	most majestic

Review Work
Write the comparative and superlative forms of the following adjectives: lucky, delightful, tame, sad, old. luckier/luckiest, more delightful/most delightful, tamer/tamest, sadder/saddest, older/oldest

Draft Book
Write 10 sentences using comparative and superlative forms of adjectives.

32

DB: Answers will vary.

Page 33

Name ______________

-Er or More — adjectives: positive, comparative, superlative

Usually, comparative and superlative adjectives are formed by adding *er* and *est*, but for a few adjectives, the spelling must be changed. Comparative and superlative adjectives can also be formed by adding the comparison words *more, most, less* or *least*. However, when using the comparative and superlative forms of an adjective do not precede the adjective with these words.

example: Divya is smarter. (yes)
Divya is more smarter. (no)
Divya is most smarter. (no)

Circle the correct adjectives.

The (nearest, more nearest) restaurant is four miles away.

This hot chocolate is (hotter, most hot) than I like it.

My friend Preeti is the (most nicer, nicest) person I know.

That movie is (more interesting, interestinger) than the one we watched last week.

This book is (less intenser, less intense) than its sequel.

This assignment is (harder, more harder) than yesterday's was.

The (best, more best) hot dogs are those toasted on an open fire.

My parents are the (least happy, least happier) when I get home late.

That batch of laddus is (sweeter, more sweeter) than this batch.

Your head is (more protecteder, more protected) with a bike helmet.

We tasted the (more worst, worst) lunch in history today.

The (most gigantic, most giganticest) spider ever just crawled across the floor.

The (older, more older) basketball is the (more better, better) ball.

Review Work
Write an *SS* above the simple subject in each sentence.

Draft Book
Write 10 sentences using comparative and superlative forms of adjectives.

33

Page 33 (cont.)

RW: Write an SS above restaurant, chocolate, Preeti, movie, book, assignment, hot dogs, parents, batch, head, we, spider and basketball.

DB: Answers will vary.

Page 34

Name ______________

Odd Adjectives — present and past participles

A participle is a verb form. It acts as an adjective. The present participle is the *ing* form of a verb. The past participle usually ends in *d* or *ed*.

examples: The **crying** baby was hungry. The **tired** child was crabby.
present participle — *past participle*

Circle each present or past participle. Draw an arrow to the noun it modifies. Write *pres* for present participle or *past* for past participle.

past — Sajia's favourite book is the battered one on the middle shelf.

pres — You must stay away from the whirling power saw blade.

past, pres — We avoided the broken glass in the parking garage.

past — The enraged hornet flew after the horse.

pres — Kamal prefers to avoid the spinning rides.

pres — Totu, the parakeet, always bothers the napping puppy.

past — The thawed desserts are in the refrigerator.

pres — Babu will blow out the burning candles.

past — Jaleel could not open the tightly closed jar.

pres — Sunit washed the serving bowl and put it away.

pres — The reading area was full, so Sam read at his desk.

past — Madhu put her muddied shoes on the deck.

Review Work
Underline the simple subjects once and the simple predicates twice.

Draft Book
Write 10 sentences that use present and past participles. Draw an arrow from each participle to the noun it modifies.

34

RW: Underline book, you, we, hornet, Kamal, Totu, desserts, Babu, Jaleel, Sunit, area and Madhu once. Underline is, stay, avoided, flew, prefers, bothers, are, blow, open, washed, was and put twice.

DB: Answers will vary.

Page 35

Name ______________

They're Confused — irregular verbs and participles

Usually, a regular verb forms the past tense and past participle by adding *d* or *ed* to the present tense verb. An irregular verb forms the past tense and past participle by changing spelling and can end with *t, en* or *n*.

examples: bite → bitten — The robber was bitten by the police dog.
freeze → frozen — The frozen yogurt was delicious.

Circle the correct verbs and participles.

The mother blue jay has (sitted, sat) on her eggs for many days.

Her (shrinked, shrunk) shirt was never worn again.

The towering, old pine had (fell, fallen) during the snowstorm.

Abhay will have (spoked, spoken) on the phone for two hours.

The girls had (swinged, swung) on the tyre swing before us.

Rohan and Preet have (swimmed, swum) in the river before.

The nanny goat at the zoo had (ate, eaten) the lace off my sock.

Tarun had (setted, set) his camera on the picnic table.

The carefully (maked, made) birthday cake was beautiful.

The fishermen had (arosed, arisen) before the sun came up.

Surabhi has (catched, caught) several monarch butterflies in her net.

That nasty hornet had (stinged, stung) Sasha's hand.

Seema and Shan have (slided, slid) down the snowy hill on their sled.

The (broke, broken) vase lay in pieces on the floor.

Review Work
Circle the plural nouns.

Draft Book
Write 10 sentences using irregular verbs. Underline the verbs with blue. Underline the nouns with yellow.

35

RW: Circle eggs, days, hours, girls, butterflies and pieces.

DB: Answers will vary.

Page 36

Name ______________

Just to Be Perfect — perfect tenses

The three perfect verb tenses indicate completed action. They are formed using the past participle (usually verb + d or ed) and the helping verbs *had, has* or *(will) have*.

past perfect: She **had known** the answer.
present perfect: She **has known** the answer.
future perfect: She **will have known** the answer.

Circle each past participle and its helping verb(s). Write *SP* for past perfect, *PP* for present perfect, or *FP* for future perfect on the line.

PP — Brinda has burnt her tongue on that hot vada.

FP — Lakshmi will have done her work.

FP — Tara will have dived off the high dive.

PP — Abhay and Tara have bitten into their apples.

FP — Laxman will have biked to the video store.

FP — The sheep will have gone to the back pasture.

PP — Kamla's cat has caught a mouse.

PP — The quarter has fallen into the drain.

SP — Anita had worked on her science project.

SP — Pran had travelled to Ajmer with Gaurav.

FP — Devi and Kris will have spoken to Ms. Sahay.

PP — The small green snake has slithered into the grass.

PP — Anil has asked for a large root beer float.

SP — The baby koala had clung to its mother's fur.

SP — Nikita had taken her craft set home.

SP — The sun had shone all week long.

Review Work
Underline the complete subjects once.

Draft Book
Write 10 sentences using the perfect tense forms of verbs. Underline the verbs with blue.

36

RW: Underline Brinda, Lakshmi, Tara, Abhay and Tara, Laxman, the sheep, Kamla's cat, the quarter, Anita, Pran, Devi and Kris, the small green snake, Anil, the baby koala, Nikita and the sun once.

DB: Answers will vary.

Page 37

Name ______________

Ongoing Action — progressive tense

The progressive verb tense indicates action in progress. It uses the present participle (verb + *ing*) and a form of the helping verb *to be*. Present progressive tense uses *am, is* and *are*. Past progressive tense uses *was* and *were*. Future progressive tense uses *will be*.

Circle each progressive verb and its helping verb(s). Write *SPg* for past, *PPg* for present or *FPg* for future on the line.

SPg — The pot of spaghetti noodles was boiling for seven minutes.

FPg — The crickets will be chirping all night long.

PPg — Sajeev is sneezing.

SPg — Abu was coughing all night.

PPg — Mala is swinging in the backyard.

PPg — The ice-cream truck is coming up the street.

FPg — The children will be swimming at the lake.

SPg — The rabbits were playing hide-and-seek with the children.

PPg — My sister Leena is knitting a sweater for my birthday.

PPg — Jairam is working on the computer.

SPg — Jameela was drinking a chocolate-milk shake.

PPg — Suman is biking to Jalil's house.

SPg — Grandma Seeta was buying produce at the farmers' market.

FPg — We will be visiting the museum on Tuesday.

PPg — Nikhil is hammering the board into the joist.

Review Work
Circle the plural nouns.

Draft Book
Write 10 sentences using progressive tense verbs. Underline the verbs with blue.

37

RW: Circle noodles, minutes, crickets, children, rabbits and children.

DB: Answers will vary.

Page 38

Name ______________

How, Where or When — adverbs

Adverbs are words that modify verbs, adjectives or other adverbs. They tell how often, where, when or to what extent something happens. Most adverbs end in *ly*. Three commonly used adverbs are *not, very* and *too*.

Circle each adverb. Indicate how it modifies by writing *how, where, when* or *what* on the line.

how — Geeta quickly finishes her paper.

when — Atul always reminds us to buckle our seat belts.

when — Nadia and I ate a large breakfast this morning.

how — The barking dog was annoyingly loud.

where — The exhausted children went inside.

when — Nath frequently drinks milk with his meals.

how — The athlete gracefully executed the flip.

what — Rohit plays too much golf.

how — Brinda silently crept up the stairs.

when — Rohini and Malar read often.

how — Lisa chatters incessantly.

where — Dad drove backward into the garage.

how — Vineet played the music quietly.

when — Rekha will work on her painting tonight.

what — The fruit salad is very healthy.

how — The plan was brilliantly thought out.

how — The storm wildly pounded the windows.

when — Devan walks daily with his friend.

Review Work
Circle the adjectives. Draw an arrow from each adjective to the noun it describes.

Draft Book
Write a story about your favourite month of the year. Include adverbs. Circle the adverbs with purple.

38

Answer Key

Page 38 (cont.)

RW; Circle large, this, barking, exhausted and fruit. Draw arrows to breakfast, morning, dog, children and salad. DB: Answers will vary.

Page 39

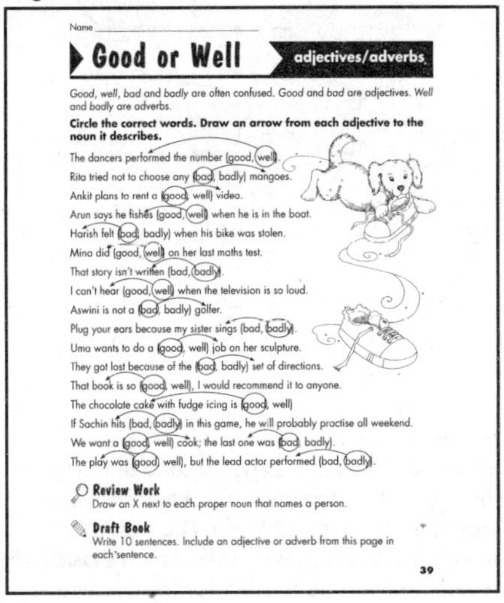

Name

Good or Well adjectives/adverbs

Good, well, bad and badly are often confused. Good and bad are adjectives. Well and badly are adverbs.

Circle the correct words. Draw an arrow from each adjective to the noun it describes.

The dancers performed the number (good, well).
Rita tried not to choose any (bad, badly) mangoes.
Ankit plans to rent a (good, well) video.
Arun says he fishes (good, well) when he is in the boat.
Harish felt (bad, badly) when his bike was stolen.
Mina did (good, well) on her last maths test.
That story isn't written (bad, badly).
I can't hear (good, well) when the television is so loud.
Aswini is not a (bad, badly) golfer.
Plug your ears because my sister sings (bad, badly).
Uma wants to do a (good, well) job on her sculpture.
They got lost because of the (bad, badly) set of directions.
That book is so (good, well), I would recommend it to anyone.
The chocolate cake with fudge icing is (good, well).
If Sachin hits (bad, badly) in this game, he will probably practise all weekend.
We want a (good, well) cook; the last one was (bad, badly).
The play was (good, well), but the lead actor performed (bad, badly).

Review Work
Draw an X next to each proper noun that names a person.

Draft Book
Write 10 sentences. Include an adjective or adverb from this page in each sentence.

39

RW: Draw an X next to Rita, Ankit, Arun, Harish, Mina, Aswini, Uma and Sachin. DB: Answers will vary.

Page 40

Answers will vary.

RW: Underline they, he, she, she, we and they with red. DB: Answers will vary.

Page 41

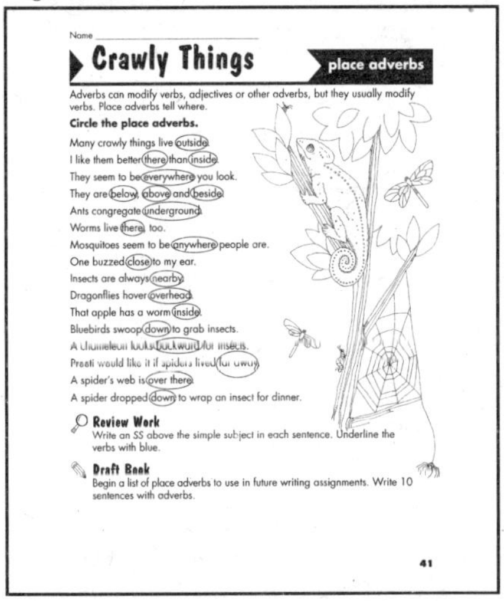

Name

Crawly Things place adverbs

Adverbs can modify verbs, adjectives or other adverbs, but they usually modify verbs. Place adverbs tell where.

Circle the place adverbs.

Many crawly things live (outside).
I like them better (there) than (inside).
They seem to be (everywhere) you look.
They are (below), (above) and (beside).
Ants congregate (underground).
Worms live (there) too.
Mosquitoes seem to be (anywhere) people are.
One buzzed (close) to my ear.
Insects are always (nearby).
Dragonflies hover (overhead).
That apple has a worm (inside).
Bluebirds swoop (down) to grab insects.
A chameleon looks (outward) for insects.
Preeti would like it if spiders lived (far away).
A spider's web is (over there).
A spider dropped (down) to wrap an insect for dinner.

Review Work
Write an SS above the simple subject in each sentence. Underline the verbs with blue.

Draft Book
Begin a list of place adverbs to use in future writing assignments. Write 10 sentences with adverbs.

41

RW: Write an SS above things, I, they, they, ants, worms, mosquitoes, one, insects, dragonflies, apple, bluebirds, chameleon, Preeti, web and spider. Underline live, like, seem, are, congregate, live, seem, buzzed, are, hover, has, swoop, looks, would like, is and dropped with blue.

DB: Answers will vary.

Page 42

Name

How'd You Do That? manner adverbs

Adverbs can modify verbs, adjectives or other adverbs, but they usually modify verbs. Manner adverbs tell how or in what manner an action is performed. Many end in ly.

Circle each manner adverb. Draw an arrow to the verb it modifies.

The kitten and puppy (playfully) ran from one end of the room to the other.
Julie appeared (calm) but one foot tapped (nervously).
Liza smiled (confidently) as she waved good-bye to her parents.
The children waited (expectantly) for the movie to begin.
Many fireworks exploded (simultaneously) in the night sky.
Louis likes to read (aloud) to the kindergartners.
Ahmed and I walked (together) to football practice.
We were (completely) surprised by the announcement.
Roshan worked (diligently) to finish his project by Friday.
Susie (carefully) climbed the maple tree to get the kitten down.
Alok (quickly) rode his bike home in order to meet his curfew.
Minu (regretfully) completed the exciting book.
Harish (intently) watched the ants carry load after load into the anthill.
Uma (maliciously) tore Smita's artwork.
Prema (immediately) doused the paper fire with water.

Review Work
Underline the nouns with yellow.

Draft Book
Begin a list of manner adverbs to use in future writing assignments. Write 10 sentences with adverbs.

42

RW: Underline kitten, puppy, end, room, Julie, foot, Liza, parents, children, movie, fireworks, sky, Louis, kindergarteners, Ahmed, practice, announcement, Roshan, project, Friday, Susie, tree, kitten, Alok, bike, curfew, Minu, book, Harish, ants, load, anthill, Uma, artwork, Prema, fire and water with yellow.

DB: Answers will vary.

Page 43

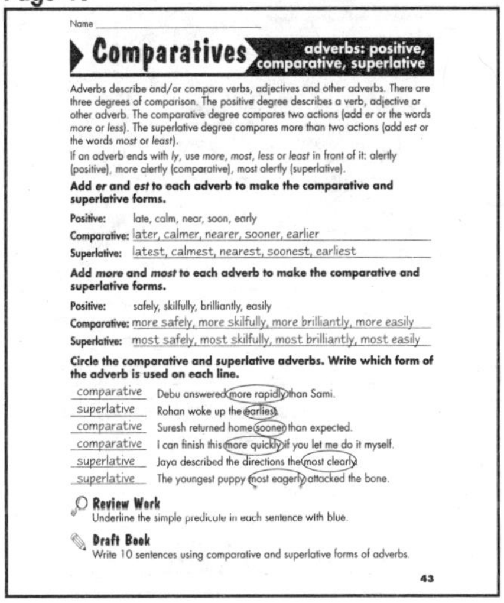

Name

Comparatives adverbs: positive, comparative, superlative

Adverbs describe and/or compare verbs, adjectives and other adverbs. There are three degrees of comparison. The positive degree describes a verb, adjective or other adverb. The comparative degree compares two actions (add er or the words more or less). The superlative degree compares more than two actions (add est or the words most or least).

If an adverb ends with ly, use more, most, less or least in front of it: alertly (positive), more alertly (comparative), most alertly (superlative).

Add er and est to each adverb to make the comparative and superlative forms.

Positive: late, calm, near, soon, early
Comparative: later, calmer, nearer, sooner, earlier
Superlative: latest, calmest, nearest, soonest, earliest

Add more and most to each adverb to make the comparative and superlative forms.

Positive: safely, skilfully, brilliantly, easily
Comparative: more safely, more skilfully, more brilliantly, more easily
Superlative: most safely, most skilfully, most brilliantly, most easily

Circle the comparative and superlative adverbs. Write which form of the adverb is used on each line.

comparative — Debu answered (more rapidly) than Sami.
superlative — Rohan woke up the (earliest).
comparative — Suresh returned home (sooner) than expected.
comparative — I can finish this (more quickly) if you let me do it myself.
superlative — Joya described the directions the (most clearly).
superlative — The youngest puppy (most eagerly) attacked the bone.

Review Work
Underline the simple predicate in each sentence with blue.

Draft Book
Write 10 sentences using comparative and superlative forms of adverbs.

43

RW: Underline answered, woke, returned, finish, described and attacked with blue.

DB: Answers will vary.

Page 44

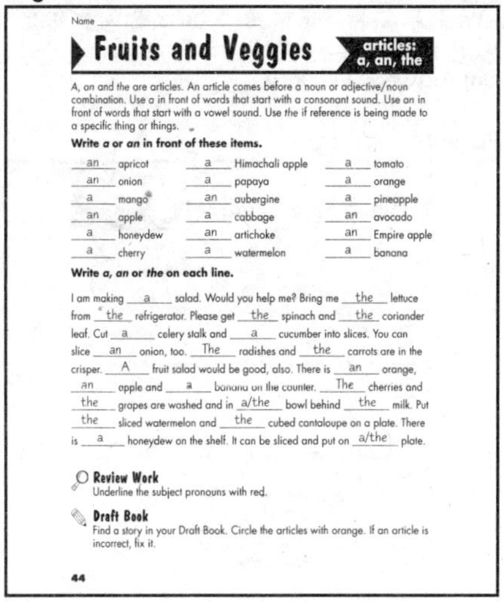

Name

Fruits and Veggies articles: a, an, the

A, an and the are articles. An article comes before a noun or adjective/noun combination. Use a in front of words that start with a consonant sound. Use an in front of words that start with a vowel sound. Use the if reference is being made to a specific thing or things.

Write a or an in front of these items.

an apricot	a Himachali apple	a tomato
an onion	a papaya	a orange
a mango	an aubergine	a pineapple
an apple	a cabbage	an avocado
a honeydew	an artichoke	an Empire apple
a cherry	a watermelon	a banana

Write a, an or the on each line.

I am making a salad. Would you help me? Bring me the lettuce from the refrigerator. Please get the spinach and the coriander leaf. Cut a celery stalk and a cucumber into slices. You can slice an onion, too. The radishes and the carrots are in the crisper. A fruit salad would be good, also. There is an orange, an apple and a banana on the counter. The cherries and the grapes are washed and in a/the bowl behind the milk. Put the sliced watermelon and the cubed cantaloupe on a plate. There is a honeydew on the shelf. It can be sliced and put on a/the plate.

Review Work
Underline the subject pronouns with red.

Draft Book
Find a story in your Draft Book. Circle the articles with orange. If an article is incorrect, fix it.

44

RW: Underline I, you, you and it with red. DB: Answers will vary.

Page 45

Name

The Entire Thing complete subject

The simple subject is the noun that the sentence is about. The complete subject is the simple subject plus any articles or adjectives that describe or modify that noun.

example: The striped ball rolled down the hill.
ball = simple subject
The striped ball = complete subject
article adjective

Circle the simple subjects. Underline the complete subjects.

An itsy-bitsy (bug) will crawl under your beach towel.
Those five scary (costumes) were chosen for the play.
That incredibly high (roller coaster) causes people to scream.
The earsplitting (tornado) rampaged through town.
Those sharp (knives) have protective covers on them.
Our old, battered road (atlas) helped us determine travel routes.
Those neon-coloured (crayons) add vibrant details to pictures.
My icy-cold (fingers) will need a pair of warm gloves.
Minu's little (sister) played the game all afternoon.
That very long (number) is not a palindrome.
Kunal's sunburnt (shoulders) hurt.
(Saravan) moved to Chennai.
That smelly (lotion) tingles on my skin.
The luminescent (insects) flickered on and off in the quiet darkness.

Review Work
Underline the simple predicates with blue. Write the verb tense beside each sentence: S = past, P = present and F = future.

Draft Book
Write 10 sentences. Circle the simple subjects and underline the complete subjects.

45

RW: Underline crawl, chosen, causes, rampaged, have, helped, add, need, played, is, hurt, moved, tingles and flickered with blue.

1. F 2. F 3. P 4. S 5. P 6. S 7. P 8. F 9. S 10. P 11. P 12. S 13. P 14. S

DB: Answers will vary.

Page 46

Name

Get the Rest complete predicate

The simple predicate is the verb that tells what someone or something is doing. The complete predicate is the simple predicate plus any helping or linking verbs and any adverbs that describe or modify the verb.

example: The marble can roll smoothly.
roll = simple predicate
can roll smoothly = complete predicate
helping verb adverb

Circle the simple predicates. Underline the complete predicates.

The black and brown puppy may have been (bought) already.
That spotted dog often (races) around.
A hornet will (sting) quickly.
Little brown tree frogs (buzz) continuously.
The colourful parrot (squawked) most loudly.
The little golden hamster (scurries) around.
Mourning doves will (wake) up earliest.
The marble-sized hail suddenly (pounded) down.
The glowing coals (shimmered) more brightly.
Dolphins must (surface) often.
The number four race car (accelerated) rapidly.
Aamir often (works) slowly but accurately.
That large stain will (need) prompt attention.
This disgusting tasting medicine was (swallowed) very quickly.

Review Work
Indicate the verb tense used in each sentence. Write the verb tense beside each sentence: S = past, P = present and F = future.

Draft Book
Write 10 sentences with helping verbs and adverbs modifying the simple predicates. Underline the complete predicates with blue.

46

Answer Key

Page 46 (cont.)

RW: 1. S 2. P 3. F 4. P 5. S 6. P 7. F 8. S 9. S 10. P 11. S 12. P 13. F 14. S

DB: Answers will vary.

Page 47

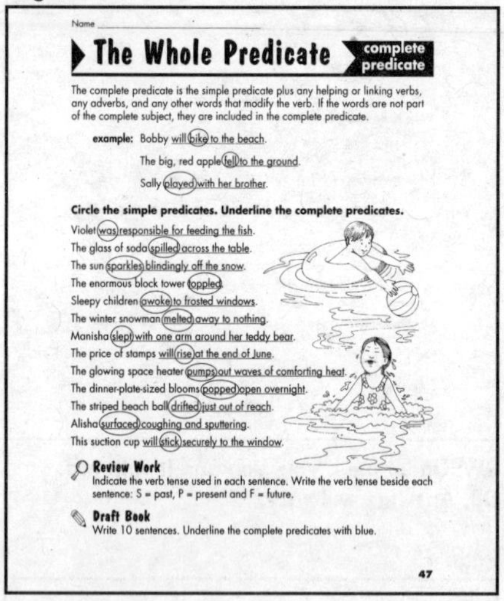
Name

The Whole Predicate — complete predicate

The complete predicate is the simple predicate plus any helping or linking verbs, any adverbs, and any other words that modify the verb. If the words are not part of the complete subject, they are included in the complete predicate.

example: Bobby will bike to the beach.
The big, red apple fell to the ground.
Sally played with her brother.

Circle the simple predicates. Underline the complete predicates.

Violet was responsible for feeding the fish.
The glass of soda spilled across the table.
The sun sparkles blindingly off the snow.
The enormous block tower toppled.
Sleepy children awoke to frosted windows.
The winter snowman melted away to nothing.
Manisha slept with one arm around her teddy bear.
The price of stamps will rise at the end of June.
The glowing space heater pumps out waves of comforting heat.
The dinner-plate-sized blooms popped open overnight.
The striped beach ball drifted just out of reach.
Alisha surfaced coughing and sputtering.
This suction cup will stick securely to the window.

Review Work
Indicate the verb tense used in each sentence. Write the verb tense beside each sentence: S = past, P = present and F = future.

Draft Book
Write 10 sentences. Underline the complete predicates with blue.

47

RW: 1. S 2. S 3. P 4. S 5. S 6. S 7. S 8. F 9. P 10. S 11. S 12. S 13. F

DB: Answers will vary.

Page 48

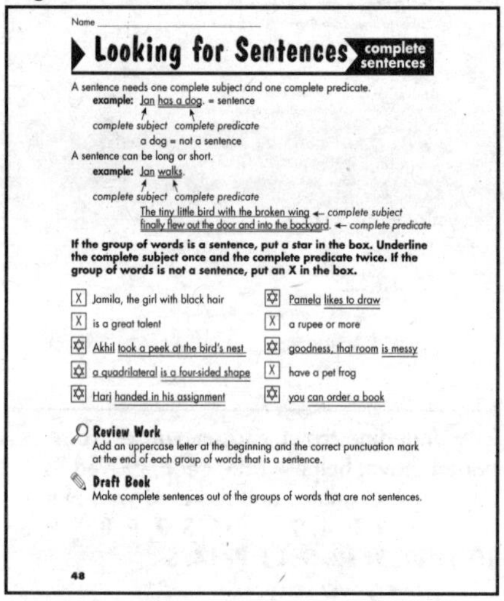
Name

Looking for Sentences — complete sentences

A sentence needs one complete subject and one complete predicate.
example: Jan has a dog. = sentence
complete subject complete predicate
a dog = not a sentence
A sentence can be long or short.
example: Jan walks.
complete subject complete predicate
The tiny little bird with the broken wing ← complete subject
finally flew out the door and into the backyard. ← complete predicate

If the group of words is a sentence, put a star in the box. Underline the complete subject once and the complete predicate twice. If the group of words is not a sentence, put an X in the box.

X Jamila, the girl with black hair — ☆ Pamela likes to draw
X is a great talent — X a rupee or more
☆ Akhil took a peek at the bird's nest — ☆ goodness, that room is messy
☆ a quadrilateral is a four-sided shape — X have a pet frog
☆ Hari handed in his assignment — ☆ you can order a book

Review Work
Add an uppercase letter at the beginning and the correct punctuation mark at the end of each group of words that is a sentence.

Draft Book
Make complete sentences out of the groups of words that are not sentences.

48

RW: Add correct beginning uppercase letter and ending punctuation to each sentence.
DB: Answers will vary.

Page 49
Answers will vary.

Page 50

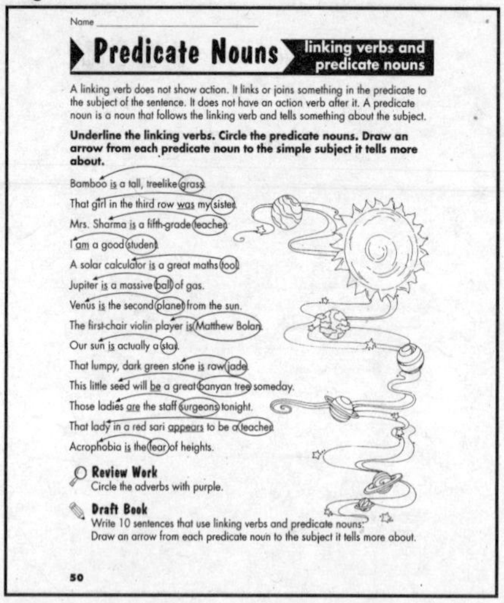
Name

Predicate Nouns — linking verbs and predicate nouns

A linking verb does not show action. It links or joins something in the predicate to the subject of the sentence. It does not have an action verb after it. A predicate noun is a noun that follows the linking verb and tells something about the subject.

Underline the linking verbs. Circle the predicate nouns. Draw an arrow from each predicate noun to the simple subject it tells more about.

Bamboo is a tall, treelike grass.
That girl in the third row was my sister.
Mrs. Sharma is a fifth-grade teacher.
I am a good student.
A solar calculator is a great maths tool.
Jupiter is a massive ball of gas.
Venus is the second planet from the sun.
The first-chair violin player is Matthew Bolan.
Our sun is actually a star.
That lumpy, dark green stone is raw jade.
This little seed will be a great banyan tree someday.
Those ladies are the staff surgeons tonight.
That lady in a red sari appears to be a teacher.
Acrophobia is the fear of heights.

Review Work
Circle the adverbs with purple.

Draft Book
Write 10 sentences that use linking verbs and predicate nouns.
Draw an arrow from each predicate noun to the subject it tells more about.

50

RW: Circle originally, actually, someday and tonight with purple. DB: Answers will vary.

Page 51

Name

Summertime — linking verbs and predicate adjectives

A linking verb does not show action. It links or joins something in the predicate to the subject of the sentence. It does not have an action verb after it. A predicate adjective is an adjective that follows the linking verb and tells something about the subject.

Underline the linking verbs. Circle the predicate adjectives. Draw an arrow from each predicate adjective to the simple subject it tells more about.

Ants in the house are disgusting.
Juicy hamburgers on the grill are delicious.
That backyard deck was unvarnished.
Jenna's batting abilities are poor.
The sunburn across my shoulders is painful.
The dent from the cricket ball was sizable.
Tarun will feel sick if he eats that whole bag of candy.
Lal's back was sore from shovelling sand into the sandbox.
Mrs. Mary was enraged when she saw what those cats did to her garbage.
Vineet and I were unhappy with our performance on the tennis courts.
The twins were tired after swimming all afternoon.
Helping Mr. Gopal in the garden all day became boring.
The canoe trip was enjoyable.
That girl watching the otters is captivated by their antics.
That photograph is more breathtaking than your last one.
Grandmother was enchanted with the flowers we picked for her.

Review Work
Write a D above each demonstrative adjective.

Draft Book
Write 10 sentences that use linking verbs and predicate adjectives. Draw an arrow from each predicate adjective to the subject it tells more about.

51

RW: Write a D above that, that, those, that and that. DB: Answers will vary.

Page 52

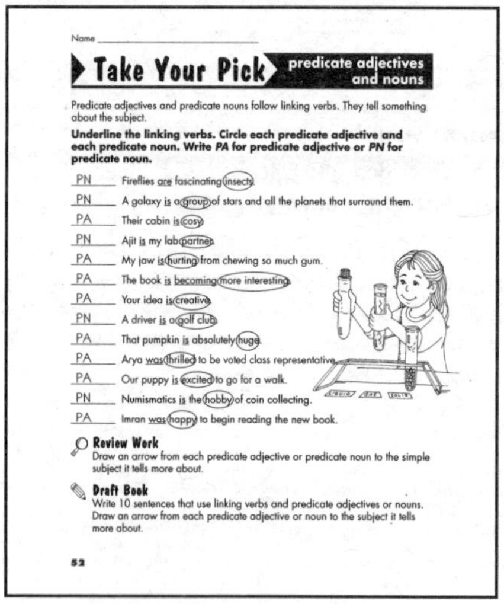
Name

Take Your Pick — predicate adjectives and nouns

Predicate adjectives and predicate nouns follow linking verbs. They tell something about the subject.

Underline the linking verbs. Circle each predicate adjective and each predicate noun. Write *PA* for predicate adjective or *PN* for predicate noun.

PN Fireflies are fascinating insects.
PN A galaxy is a group of stars and all the planets that surround them.
PA Their cabin is cosy.
PN Ajit is my lab partner.
PA My jaw is hurting from chewing so much gum.
PA The book is becoming more interesting.
PA Your idea is creative.
PN A driver is a golf club.
PA That pumpkin is absolutely huge.
PA Arya was thrilled to be voted class representative.
PA Our puppy is excited to go for a walk.
PN Numismatics is the hobby of coin collecting.
PA Imran was happy to begin reading the new book.

Review Work
Draw an arrow from each predicate adjective or predicate noun to the simple subject it tells more about.

Draft Book
Write 10 sentences that use linking verbs and predicate adjectives or nouns. Draw an arrow from each predicate adjective or noun to the subject it tells more about.

52

RW: Draw arrows to fireflies, galaxy, cabin, Ajit, jaw, book, idea, driver, pumpkin, Arya, puppy, numismatics and Imran.
DB: Answers will vary

Page 53

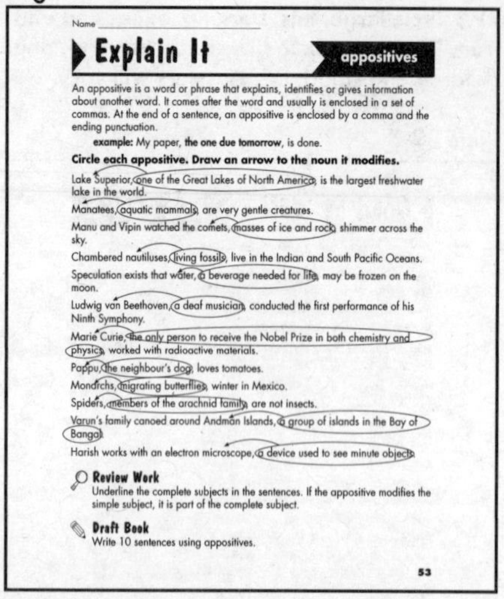
Name

Explain It — appositives

An appositive is a word or phrase that explains, identifies or gives information about another word. It comes after the word and usually is enclosed in a set of commas. At the end of a sentence, an appositive is enclosed by a comma and the ending punctuation.

example: My paper, the one due tomorrow, is done.

Circle each appositive. Draw an arrow to the noun it modifies.

Lake Superior, one of the Great Lakes of North America, is the largest freshwater lake in the world.
Manatees, aquatic mammals, are very gentle creatures.
Manu and Vipin watched the comets, masses of ice and rock, shimmer across the sky.
Chambered nautiluses, living fossils, live in the Indian and South Pacific Oceans.
Speculation exists that water, a beverage needed for life, may be frozen on the moon.
Ludwig van Beethoven, a deaf musician, conducted the first performance of his Ninth Symphony.
Marie Curie, the only person to receive the Nobel Prize in both chemistry and physics, worked with radioactive materials.
Pappu, the neighbour's dog, loves tomatoes.
Monarchs, migrating butterflies, winter in Mexico.
Spiders, members of the arachnid family, are not insects.
Varun's family canoed around Andman Islands, a group of islands in the Bay of Bangal.
Harish works with an electron microscope, a device used to see minute objects.

Review Work
Underline the complete subjects in the sentences. If the appositive modifies the simple subject, it is part of the complete subject.

Draft Book
Write 10 sentences using appositives.

53

RW: Underline Lake Superior, one of the great lakes of North America; manatees, aquatic mammals; Manu and Vipin; chambered nautiluses, living fossils; speculation exists that water, a beverage needed for life; Ludwig van Beethoven, a deaf musician; Marie Curie, the only person to receive the Nobel Prize in both chemistry and physics; Pappu, the neighbour's dog; monarchs, migrating butterflies; spiders, members of the arachnid family; Varun's family; and Harish. DB: Answers will vary.

Page 54

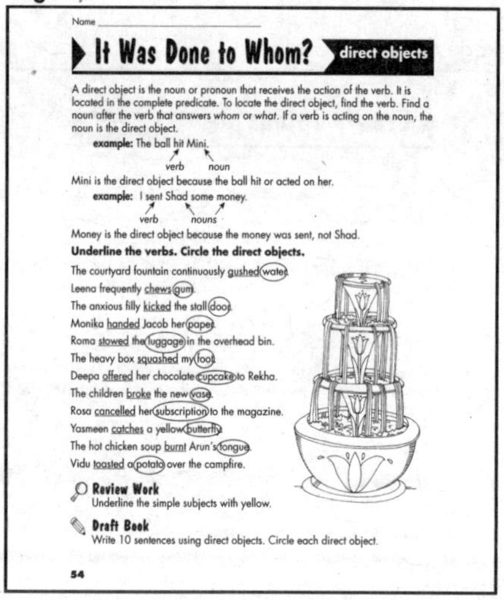
Name

It Was Done to Whom? — direct objects

A direct object is the noun or pronoun that receives the action of the verb. It is located in the complete predicate. To locate the direct object, find the verb. Find a noun after the verb that answers whom or what. If a verb is acting on the noun, the noun is the direct object.

example: The ball hit Mini.
verb noun
Mini is the direct object because the ball hit or acted on her.
example: I sent Shad some money.
verb nouns
Money is the direct object because the money was sent, not Shad.

Underline the verbs. Circle the direct objects.

The courtyard fountain continuously gushed water.
Leena frequently chews gum.
The anxious filly kicked the stall door.
Monika handed Jacob her paper.
Roma stowed the luggage in the overhead bin.
The heavy box squashed my foot.
Deepa offered her chocolate cupcake to Rekha.
The children broke the new vase.
Rosa cancelled her subscription to the magazine.
Yasmeen catches a yellow butterfly.
The hot chicken soup burnt Arun's tongue.
Vidu toasted a potato over the campfire.

Review Work
Underline the simple subjects with yellow.

Draft Book
Write 10 sentences using direct objects. Circle each direct object.

54

RW: Underline fountain, Leena, filly, Monika, Roma, box, Deepa, children, Rosa, Yasmeen, soup and Vidu with yellow.
DB: Answers will vary.

Answer Key

Page 55

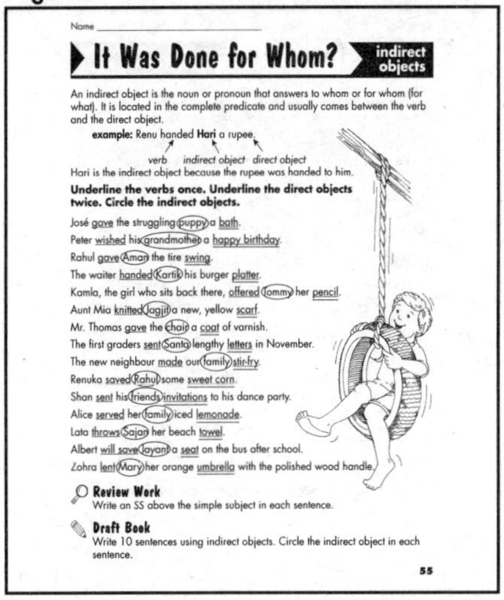

Name ______________________

It Was Done for Whom? indirect objects

An indirect object is the noun or pronoun that answers to whom or for whom (for what). It is located in the complete predicate and usually comes between the verb and the direct object.

example: Renu handed Hari a rupee.

verb   indirect object   direct object

Hari is the indirect object because the rupee was handed to him.

Underline the verbs once. Underline the direct objects twice. Circle the indirect objects.

José gave the struggling puppy a bath.
Peter wished his grandmother a happy birthday.
Rahul gave Amar the tire swing.
The waiter handed Kartik his burger platter.
Kamla, the girl who sits back there, offered Tommy her pencil.
Aunt Mia knitted Jogi a new, yellow scarf.
Mr. Thomas gave the chair a coat of varnish.
The first graders sent Santa lengthy letters in November.
The new neighbour made our family stir-fry.
Renuka saved Rahul some sweet corn.
Shan sent his friends invitations to his dance party.
Alice served her family iced lemonade.
Lata throws Sajan her beach towel.
Albert will save Jayant a seat on the bus after school.
Zohra lent Mary her orange umbrella with the polished wood handle.

Review Work
Write an SS above the simple subject in each sentence.

Draft Book
Write 10 sentences using indirect objects. Circle the indirect object in each sentence.

55

RW: Write an SS above José, Peter, Rahul, waiter, Kamla, Aunt Mia, Mr. Thomas, first graders, neighbour, Renuka, Shan, Alica, Lata, Albert and Zohra.
DB: Answers will vary.

Page 56

Answers will vary.

Page 57

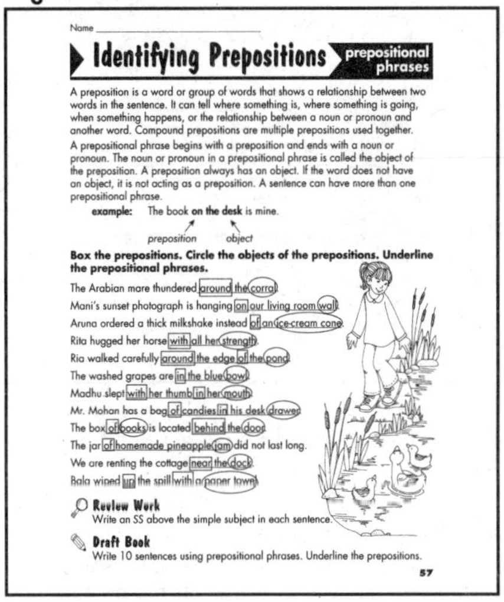

Name ______________________

Identifying Prepositions prepositional phrases

A preposition is a word or group of words that shows a relationship between two words in the sentence. It can tell where something is, where something is going, when something happens, or the relationship between a noun or pronoun and another word. Compound prepositions are multiple prepositions used together.
A prepositional phrase begins with a preposition and ends with a noun or pronoun. The noun or pronoun in a prepositional phrase is called the object of the preposition. A preposition always has an object. If the word does not have an object, it is not acting as a preposition. A sentence can have more than one prepositional phrase.

example: The book on the desk is mine.

preposition   object

Box the prepositions. Circle the objects of the prepositions. Underline the prepositional phrases.

The Arabian mare thundered around the corral.
Mani's sunset photograph is hanging on our living room wall.
Aruna ordered a thick milkshake instead of an ice-cream cone.
Rita hugged her horse with all her strength.
Ria walked carefully around the edge of the pond.
The washed grapes are in the blue bowl.
Madhu slept with her thumb in her mouth.
Mr. Mohan has a bag of candies in his desk drawer.
The box of books is located behind the door.
The jar of homemade pineapple jam did not last long.
We are renting the cottage near the dock.
Bala wiped up the spill with a paper towel.

Review Work
Write an SS above the simple subject in each sentence.

Draft Book
Write 10 sentences using prepositional phrases. Underline the prepositions.

57

RW: Write an SS above mare, photograph, Aruna, Rita, Ria, grapes, Madhu, Mr. Mohan, box, jar, we and Bala.
DB: Answers will vary.

Page 58

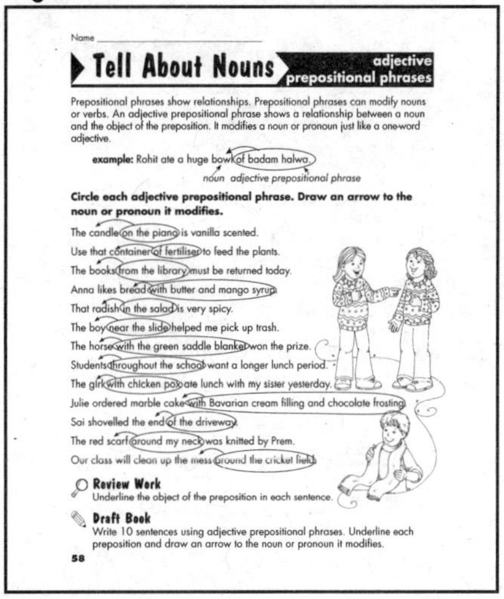

Name ______________________

Tell About Nouns adjective prepositional phrases

Prepositional phrases show relationships. Prepositional phrases can modify nouns or verbs. An adjective prepositional phrase shows a relationship between a noun and the object of the preposition. It modifies a noun or pronoun just like a one-word adjective.

example: Rohit ate a huge bowl of badam halwa.

noun   adjective prepositional phrase

Circle each adjective prepositional phrase. Draw an arrow to the noun or pronoun it modifies.

The candle on the piano is vanilla scented.
Use that container of fertiliser to feed the plants.
The books from the library must be returned today.
Anna likes bread with butter and mango syrup.
That radish in the salad is very spicy.
The boy near the slide helped me pick up trash.
The horse with the green saddle blanket won the prize.
Students throughout the school want a longer lunch period.
The girl with chicken pox ate lunch with my sister yesterday.
Julie ordered marble cake with Bavarian cream filling and chocolate frosting.
Soi shovelled the end of the driveway.
The red scarf around my neck was knitted by Prem.
Our class will clean up the mess around the cricket field.

Review Work
Underline the object of the preposition in each sentence.

Draft Book
Write 10 sentences using adjective prepositional phrases. Underline each preposition and draw an arrow to the noun or pronoun it modifies.

58

RW: Underline piano, fertiliser, library, butter, mango syrup, salad, slide, blanket, filling, frosting, school, chicken pox, driveway, neck and field. DB: Answers will vary.

Page 59

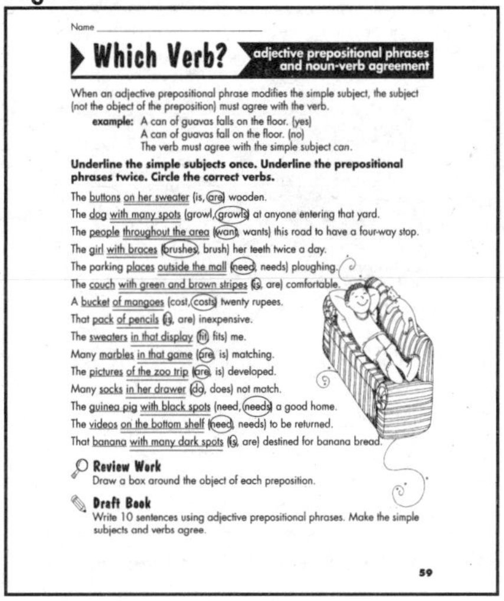

Name ______________________

Which Verb? adjective prepositional phrases and noun-verb agreement

When an adjective prepositional phrase modifies the simple subject, the subject (not the object of the preposition) must agree with the verb.

example: A can of guavas falls on the floor. (yes)
A can of guavas fall on the floor. (no)
The verb must agree with the simple subject can.

Underline the simple subjects once. Underline the prepositional phrases twice. Circle the correct verbs.

The buttons on her sweater (is, are) wooden.
The dog with many spots (growl, growls) at anyone entering that yard.
The people throughout the area (want, wants) this road to have a four-way stop.
The girl with braces (brushes, brush) her teeth twice a day.
The parking places outside the mall (need, needs) ploughing.
The couch with green and brown stripes (is, are) comfortable.
A bucket of mangoes (cost, costs) twenty rupees.
That pack of pencils (is, are) inexpensive.
The sweaters in that display (fit, fits) me.
Many marbles in that game (are, is) matching.
The pictures of the zoo trip (are, is) developed.
Many socks in her drawer (do, does) not match.
The guinea pig with black spots (need, needs) a good home.
The videos on the bottom shelf (need, needs) to be returned.
That banana with many dark spots (is, are) destined for banana bread.

Review Work
Draw a box around the object of each preposition.

Draft Book
Write 10 sentences using adjective prepositional phrases. Make the simple subjects and verbs agree.

59

RW: Draw a box around sweater, spots, area, braces, mall, stripes, blueberries, pencils, display, game, trip, drawer, spots, shelf and spots. DB: Answers will vary.

Page 60

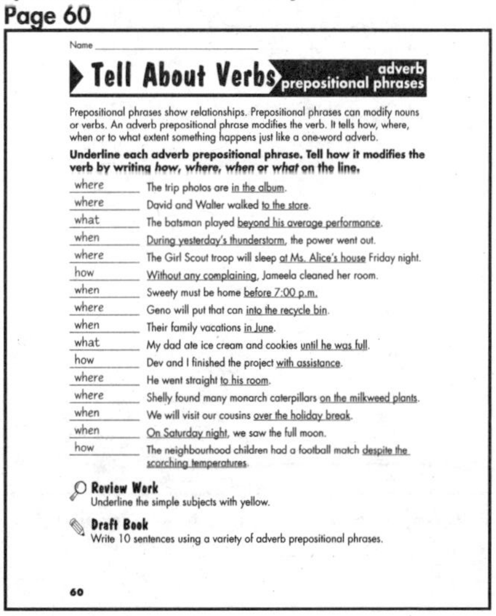

Name ______________________

Tell About Verbs adverb prepositional phrases

Prepositional phrases show relationships. Prepositional phrases can modify nouns or verbs. An adverb prepositional phrase modifies the verb. It tells how, where, when or to what extent something happens just like a one-word adverb.

Underline each adverb prepositional phrase. Tell how it modifies the verb by writing *how, where, when* or *what* on the line.

where — The trip photos are in the album.
where — David and Walter walked to the store.
what — The batsman played beyond his average performance.
when — During yesterday's thunderstorm, the power went out.
where — The Girl Scout troop will sleep at Ms. Alice's house Friday night.
how — Without any complaining, Jameela cleaned her room.
when — Sweety must be home before 7:00 p.m.
where — Geno will put that can into the recycle bin.
when — Their family vacations in June.
what — My dad ate ice cream and cookies until he was full.
how — Dev and I finished the project with assistance.
where — He went straight to his room.
where — Shelly found many monarch caterpillars on the milkweed plants.
when — We will visit our cousins over the holiday break.
when — On Saturday night, we saw the full moon.
how — The neighbourhood children had a football match despite the scorching temperatures.

Review Work
Underline the simple subjects with yellow.

Draft Book
Write 10 sentences using a variety of adverb prepositional phrases.

60

Page 60 (cont.)

RW: Underline photos, David, Walter, batsman, power, troop, Jameela, Sweety, Geno, family, dad, Dev, I, he, Shelly, we, we and children with yellow.DB: Answers will vary.

Page 61

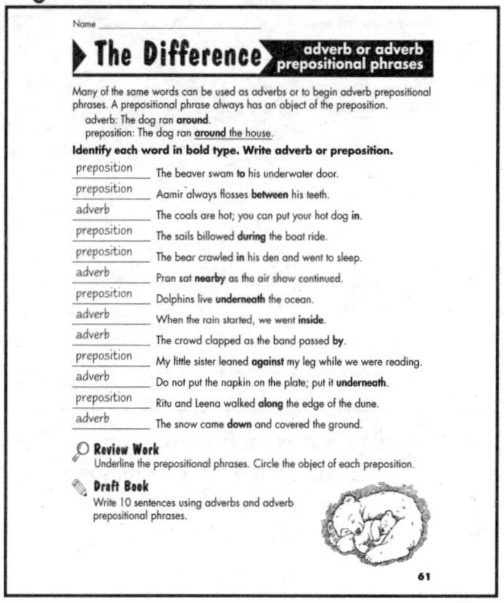

Name ______________________

The Difference adverb or adverb prepositional phrases

Many of the same words can be used as adverbs or to begin adverb prepositional phrases. A prepositional phrase always has an object of the preposition.
adverb: The dog ran around.
preposition: The dog ran around the house.

Identify each word in bold type. Write adverb or preposition.

preposition — The beaver swam **to** his underwater door.
preposition — Aamir always flosses **between** his teeth.
adverb — The coals are hot; you can put your hot dog **in**.
preposition — The sails billowed **during** the boat ride.
preposition — The bear crawled **in** his den and went to sleep.
adverb — Pran sat **nearby** as the air show continued.
preposition — Dolphins live **underneath** the ocean.
adverb — When the rain started, we went **inside**.
adverb — The crowd clapped as the band passed **by**.
preposition — My little sister leaned **against** my leg while we were reading.
adverb — Do not put the napkin on the plate; put it **underneath**.
preposition — Ritu and Leena walked **along** the edge of the dune.
adverb — The snow came **down** and covered the ground.

Review Work
Underline the prepositional phrases. Circle the object of each preposition.

Draft Book
Write 10 sentences using adverbs and adverb prepositional phrases.

61

RW: Underline to his underwater door, between his teeth, during the boat ride, in his den, underneath the ocean, against my leg and along the edge. Circle door, teeth, ride, den, ocean, leg and edge.
DB: Answers will vary.

Page 62

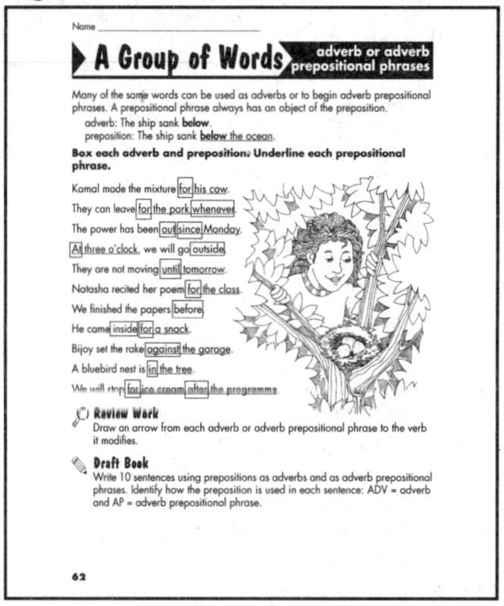

Name ______________________

A Group of Words adverb or adverb prepositional phrases

Many of the same words can be used as adverbs or to begin adverb prepositional phrases. A prepositional phrase always has an object of the preposition.
adverb: The ship sank below.
preposition: The ship sank below the ocean.

Box each adverb and preposition. Underline each prepositional phrase.

Kamal made the mixture for his cow.
They can leave for the park whenever.
The power has been out since Monday.
At three o'clock, we will go outside.
They are not moving until tomorrow.
Natasha recited her poem for the class.
We finished the papers before.
He came inside for a snack.
Bijoy set the rake against the garage.
A bluebird nest is in the tree.
We will stop for ice cream after the programme.

Review Work
Draw an arrow from each adverb or adverb prepositional phrase to the verb it modifies.

Draft Book
Write 10 sentences using prepositions as adverbs and as adverb prepositional phrases. Identify how the preposition is used in each sentence: ADV = adverb and AP = adverb prepositional phrase.

62

RW: Draw arrows to made, leave, has been, go, moving, recited, finished, came, set, is and stop. DB: Answers will vary.

Answer Key

Page 63

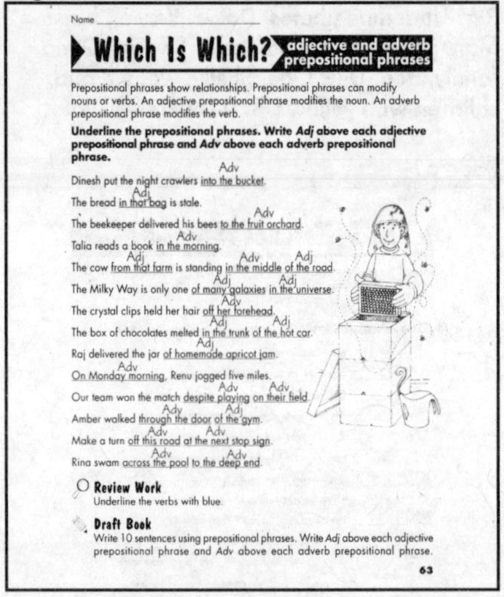
Name ______

Which Is Which? adjective and adverb prepositional phrases

Prepositional phrases show relationships. Prepositional phrases can modify nouns or verbs. An adjective prepositional phrase modifies the noun. An adverb prepositional phrase modifies the verb.

Underline the prepositional phrases. Write *Adj* above each adjective prepositional phrase and *Adv* above each adverb prepositional phrase.

Dinesh put the night crawlers into the bucket. (Adv)
The bread in that bag is stale. (Adj)
The beekeeper delivered his bees to the fruit orchard. (Adv)
Talia reads a book in the morning. (Adv)
The cow from that farm is standing in the middle of the road. (Adj, Adv, Adj)
The Milky Way is only one of many galaxies in the universe. (Adj, Adj)
The crystal clips held her hair off her forehead. (Adv)
The box of chocolates melted in the trunk of the hot car. (Adj, Adv, Adj)
Raj delivered the jar of homemade apricot jam. (Adj)
On Monday morning, Renu jogged five miles. (Adv)
Our team won the match despite playing on their field. (Adv, Adv)
Amber walked through the door of the gym. (Adv, Adj)
Make a turn off this road at the next stop sign. (Adv, Adv)
Rina swam across the pool to the deep end. (Adv, Adv)

Review Work Underline the verbs with blue.

Draft Book Write 10 sentences using prepositional phrases. Write Adj above each adjective prepositional phrase and Adv above each adverb prepositional phrase.

63

RW: Underline put, is, delivered, reads, is, standing, is, held, melted, delivered, jogged, won, walked, make and swam.
DB: Answers will vary.

Page 64

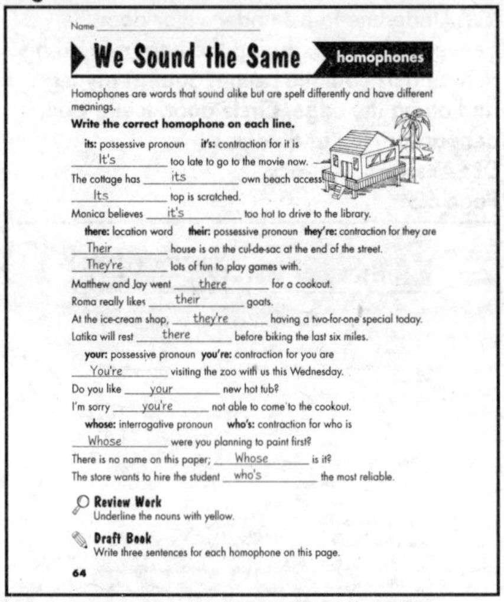
Name ______

We Sound the Same homophones

Homophones are words that sound alike but are spelt differently and have different meanings.

Write the correct homophone on each line.

its: possessive pronoun **it's:** contraction for it is
It's too late to go to the movie now.
The cottage has its own beach access.
Its top is scratched.
Monica believes it's too hot to drive to the library.

there: location word **their:** possessive pronoun **they're:** contraction for they are
Their house is on the cul-de-sac at the end of the street.
They're lots of fun to play games with.
Matthew and Jay went there for a cookout.
Roma really likes their goats.
At the ice-cream shop, they're having a two-for-one special today.
Latika will rest there before biking the last six miles.

your: possessive pronoun **you're:** contraction for you are
You're visiting the zoo with us this Wednesday.
Do you like your new hot tub?
I'm sorry you're not able to come to the cookout.

whose: interrogative pronoun **who's:** contraction for who is
Whose were you planning to paint first?
There is no name on this paper; Whose is it?
The store wants to hire the student who's the most reliable.

Review Work Underline the nouns with yellow.

Draft Book Write three sentences for each homophone on this page.

64

RW: Underline movie, cottage, access, top, Monica, library, house, cul-de-sac, end, street, fun, games, Matthew, Jay, cookout, Roma, goats, shop, special, Latika, miles, zoo, Wednesday, hot tub, cookout, name, paper, store and student.
DB: Answers will vary.

Page 65
Answers will vary.

Page 66

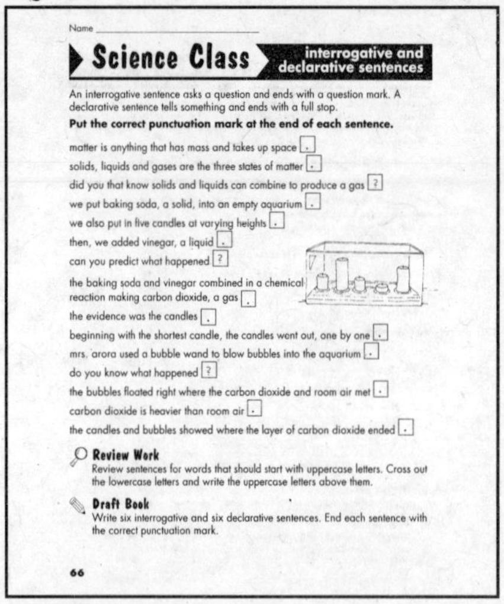
Name ______

Science Class interrogative and declarative sentences

An interrogative sentence asks a question and ends with a question mark. A declarative sentence tells something and ends with a full stop.

Put the correct punctuation mark at the end of each sentence.

matter is anything that has mass and takes up space [.]
solids, liquids and gases are the three states of matter [.]
did you that know solids and liquids can combine to produce a gas [?]
we put baking soda, a solid, into an empty aquarium [.]
we also put in five candles at varying heights [.]
then, we added vinegar, a liquid [.]
can you predict what happened [?]
the baking soda and vinegar combined in a chemical reaction making carbon dioxide, a gas [.]
the evidence was the candles [.]
beginning with the shortest candle, the candles went out, one by one [.]
mrs. arora used a bubble wand to blow bubbles into the aquarium [.]
do you know what happened [?]
the bubbles floated right where the carbon dioxide and room air met [.]
carbon dioxide is heavier than room air [.]
the candles and bubbles showed where the layer of carbon dioxide ended [.]

Review Work Review sentences for words that should start with uppercase letters. Cross out the lowercase letters and write the uppercase letters above them.

Draft Book Write six interrogative and six declarative sentences. End each sentence with the correct punctuation mark.

66

RW: Add uppercase letters where necessary.
DB: Answers will vary.

Page 67

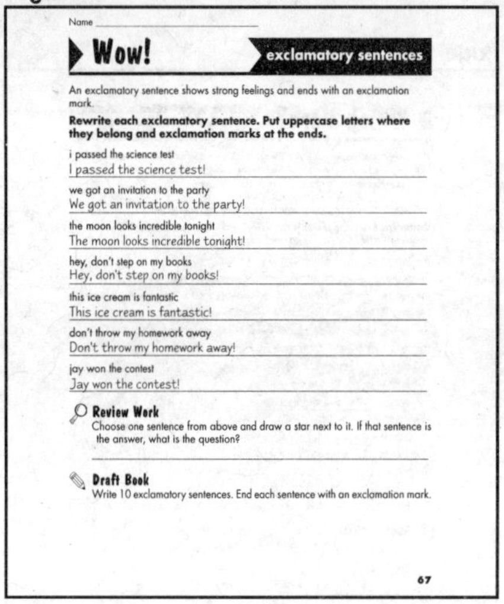
Name ______

Wow! exclamatory sentences

An exclamatory sentence shows strong feelings and ends with an exclamation mark.

Rewrite each exclamatory sentence. Put uppercase letters where they belong and exclamation marks at the ends.

i passed the science test
I passed the science test!
we got an invitation to the party
We got an invitation to the party!
the moon looks incredible tonight
The moon looks incredible tonight!
hey, don't step on my books
Hey, don't step on my books!
this ice cream is fantastic
This ice cream is fantastic!
don't throw my homework away
Don't throw my homework away!
jay won the contest
Jay won the contest!

Review Work Choose one sentence from above and draw a star next to it. If that sentence is the answer, what is the question?

Draft Book Write 10 exclamatory sentences. End each sentence with an exclamation mark.

67

RW: Answers will vary. DB: Answers will vary.

Page 68

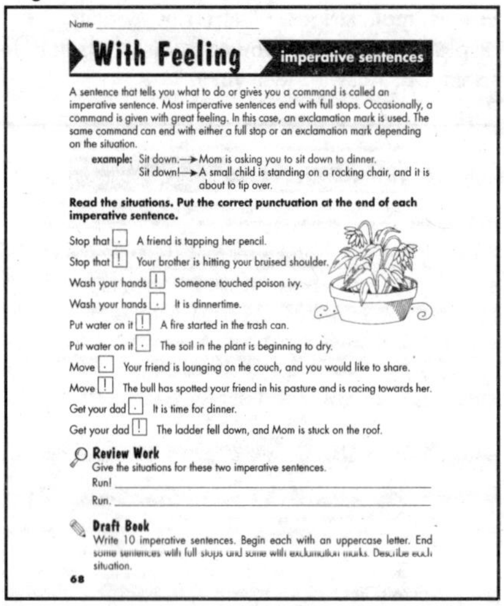
Name ______

With Feeling imperative sentences

A sentence that tells you what to do or gives you a command is called an imperative sentence. Most imperative sentences end with full stops. Occasionally, a command is given with great feeling. In this case, an exclamation mark is used. The same command can end with either a full stop or an exclamation mark depending on the situation.

example: Sit down.→Mom is asking you to sit down to dinner.
Sit down!→A small child is standing on a rocking chair, and it is about to tip over.

Read the situations. Put the correct punctuation at the end of each imperative sentence.

Stop that [.] A friend is tapping her pencil.
Stop that [!] Your brother is hitting your bruised shoulder.
Wash your hands [!] Someone touched poison ivy.
Wash your hands [.] It is dinnertime.
Put water on it [!] A fire started in the trash can.
Put water on it [.] The soil in the plant is beginning to dry.
Move [.] Your friend is lounging on the couch, and you would like to share.
Move [!] The bull has spotted your friend in his pasture and is racing towards her.
Get your dad [.] It is time for dinner.
Get your dad [!] The ladder fell down, and Mom is stuck on the roof.

Review Work Give the situations for these two imperative sentences.
Run! ______
Run. ______

Draft Book Write 10 imperative sentences. Begin each with an uppercase letter. End some sentences with full stops and some with exclamation marks. Describe each situation.

68

RW: Answers will vary. DB: Answers will vary.

Page 69

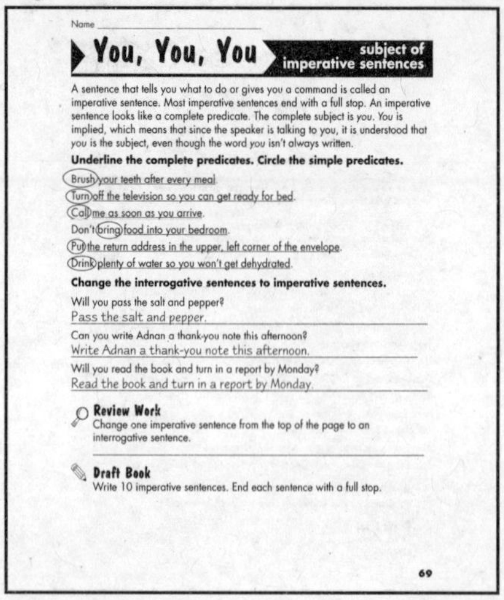
Name ______

You, You, You subject of imperative sentences

A sentence that tells you what to do or gives you a command is called an imperative sentence. Most imperative sentences end with a full stop. An imperative sentence looks like a complete predicate. The complete subject is *you*. You is implied, which means that since the speaker is talking to you, it is understood that you is the subject, even though the word you isn't always written.

Underline the complete predicates. Circle the simple predicates.

(Brush) your teeth after every meal.
(Turn) off the television so you can get ready for bed.
(Call) me as soon as you arrive.
Don't (bring) food into your bedroom.
(Put) the return address in the upper, left corner of the envelope.
(Drink) plenty of water so you won't get dehydrated.

Change the interrogative sentences to imperative sentences.

Will you pass the salt and pepper?
Pass the salt and pepper.
Can you write Adnan a thank-you note this afternoon?
Write Adnan a thank-you note this afternoon.
Will you read the book and turn in a report by Monday?
Read the book and turn in a report by Monday.

Review Work Change one imperative sentence from the top of the page to an interrogative sentence.

Draft Book Write 10 imperative sentences. End each sentence with a full stop.

69

RW: Answers will vary. DB: Answers will vary.

Page 70

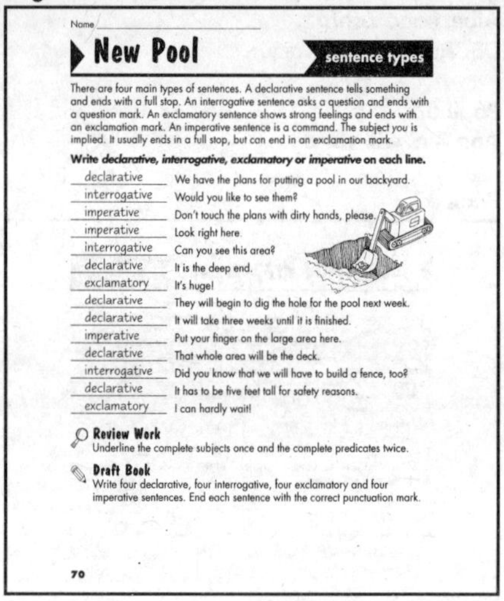
Name ______

New Pool sentence types

There are four main types of sentences. A declarative sentence tells something and ends with a full stop. An interrogative sentence asks a question and ends with a question mark. An exclamatory sentence shows strong feelings and ends with an exclamation mark. An imperative sentence is a command. The subject you is implied. It usually ends in a full stop, but can end in an exclamation mark.

Write *declarative, interrogative, exclamatory* or *imperative* on each line.

declarative — We have the plans for putting a pool in our backyard.
interrogative — Would you like to see them?
imperative — Don't touch the plans with dirty hands, please.
imperative — Look right here.
interrogative — Can you see this area?
declarative — It is the deep end.
exclamatory — It's huge!
declarative — They will begin to dig the hole for the pool next week.
declarative — It will take three weeks until it is finished.
imperative — Put your finger on the large area here.
declarative — That whole area will be the deck.
interrogative — Did you know that we will have to build a fence, too?
declarative — It has to be five feet tall for safety reasons.
exclamatory — I can hardly wait!

Review Work Underline the complete subjects once and the complete predicates twice.

Draft Book Write four declarative, four interrogative, four exclamatory and four imperative sentences. End each sentence with the correct punctuation mark.

70

Underline we, you, (you), (you), you, it, it, they, it, (you), that whole area, you, it and I once.
Underline have the plans for putting a pool in our backyard; would like to see them; don't touch the plans with dirty hands, please; look right here; can see this area; is the deep end; 's huge; will begin to dig the hole for the pool next week; will take three weeks until it is finished; put your finger on the large area here, will be the deck; did know that we will have to build a fence too; has to be five feet tall for safety reasons; and can hardly wait twice.
DB: Answers will vary.

Answer Key

Page 71

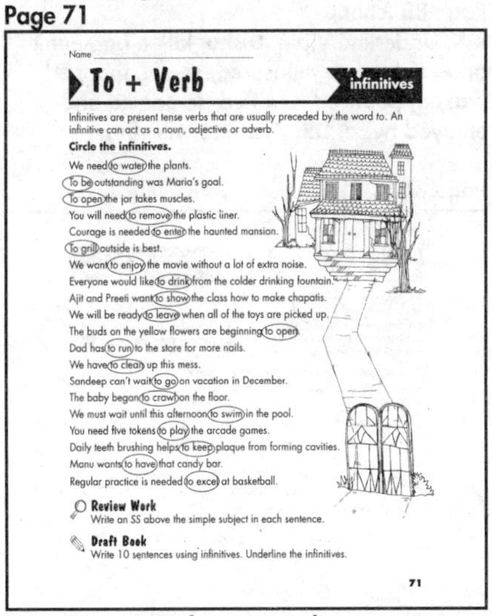

Name ______________

To + Verb — infinitives

Infinitives are present tense verbs that are usually preceded by the word to. An infinitive can act as a noun, adjective or adverb.

Circle the infinitives.

We need (to water) the plants.
(To be) outstanding was Maria's goal.
(To open) the jar takes muscles.
You will need (to remove) the plastic liner.
Courage is needed (to enter) the haunted mansion.
(To grill) outside is best.
We want (to enjoy) the movie without a lot of extra noise.
Everyone would like (to drink) from the colder drinking fountain.
Ajit and Preeti want (to show) the class how to make chapatis.
We will be ready (to leave) when all of the toys are picked up.
The buds on the yellow flowers are beginning (to open).
Dad has (to run) to the store for more nails.
We have (to clean) up this mess.
Sandeep can't wait (to go) on vacation in December.
The baby began (to crawl) on the floor.
We must wait until this afternoon (to swim) in the pool.
You need five tokens (to play) the arcade games.
Daily teeth brushing helps (to keep) plaque from forming cavities.
Manu wants (to have) that candy bar.
Regular practice is needed (to excel) at basketball.

Review Work Write an SS above the simple subject in each sentence.

Draft Book Write 10 sentences using infinitives. Underline the infinitives.

71

RW: Write an SS above we, to be, to open, you, courage, to grill, we, everyone, Ajit, Preeti, we, buds, Dad, we, Sandeep, baby, we, you, brushing, Manu and practice. DB: Answers will vary.

Page 72

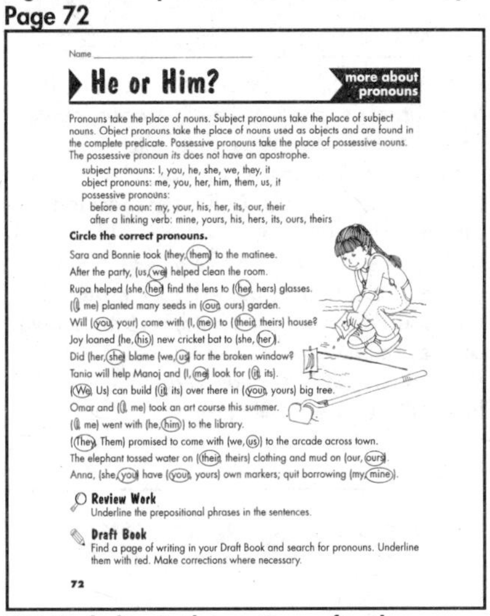

Name ______________

He or Him? — more about pronouns

Pronouns take the place of nouns. Subject pronouns take the place of subject nouns. Object pronouns take the place of nouns used as objects and are found in the complete predicate. Possessive pronouns take the place of possessive nouns. The possessive pronoun its does not have an apostrophe.

subject pronouns: I, you, he, she, we, they, it
object pronouns: me, you, her, him, them, us, it
possessive pronouns:
before a noun: my, your, his, her, its, our, their
after a linking verb: mine, yours, his, hers, its, ours, theirs

Circle the correct pronouns.

Sara and Bonnie took (they, them) to the matinee.
After the party, (us, we) helped clean the room.
Rupa helped (she, her) find the lens to (her, hers) glasses.
(I, me) planted many seeds in (our, ours) garden.
Will (you, your) come with (I, me) to (their, theirs) house?
Joy loaned (he, his) new cricket bat to (she, her).
Did (her, she) blame (we, us) for the broken window?
Tania will help Manoj and (I, me) look for (it, its).
(We, Us) can build (it, its) over there in (your, yours) big tree.
Omar and (I, me) took an art course this summer.
(I, me) went with (he, him) to the library.
(They, Them) promised to come with (we, us) to the arcade across town.
The elephant tossed water on (their, theirs) clothing and mud on (our, ours).
Anna, (she, you) have (your, yours) own markers; quit borrowing (my, mine).

Review Work Underline the prepositional phrases in the sentences.

Draft Book Find a page of writing in your Draft Book and search for pronouns. Underline them with red. Make corrections where necessary.

72

RW: Underline to the matinee, after the snowstorm, to her glasses, in our garden, with me, to their house, to her, for the broken window, for it, over there, in your big tree, with him, to the library, to come, with us, to the arcade, across town, on their clothing and on ours. DB: Answers will vary.

Page 73

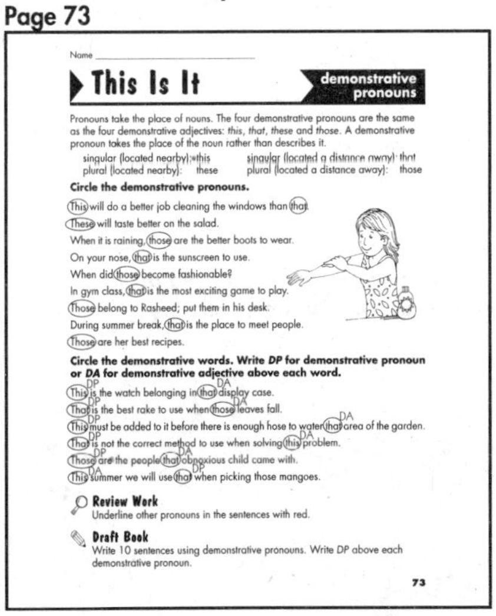

Name ______________

This Is It — demonstrative pronouns

Pronouns take the place of nouns. The four demonstrative pronouns are the same as the four demonstrative adjectives: this, that, these and those. A demonstrative pronoun takes the place of the noun rather than describes it.

singular (located nearby): this — singular (located a distance away): that
plural (located nearby): these — plural (located a distance away): those

Circle the demonstrative pronouns.

(This) will do a better job cleaning the windows than (that).
(These) will taste better on the salad.
When it is raining, (those) are the better boots to wear.
On your nose, (that) is the sunscreen to use.
When did (those) become fashionable?
In gym class, (that) is the most exciting game to play.
(Those) belong to Rasheed; put them in his desk.
During summer break, (that) is the place to meet people.
(Those) are her best recipes.

Circle the demonstrative words. Write DP for demonstrative pronoun or DA for demonstrative adjective above each word.

(This) [DP] is the watch belonging in (that) [DA] display case.
(That) [DP] is the best rake to use when (those) [DA] leaves fall.
(This) [DP] must be added to it before there is enough hose to water (that) [DA] area of the garden.
(That) [DP] is not the correct method to use when solving (this) [DA] problem.
(Those) [DP] are the people (that) [DA] obnoxious child came with.
(This) [DA] summer we will use (that) [DP] when picking those mangoes.

Review Work Underline other pronouns in the sentences with red.

Draft Book Write 10 sentences using demonstrative pronouns. Write DP above each demonstrative pronoun.

73

Page 73 (cont.)

RW: Underline it, your, them, his, her and we with red. DB: Answers will vary

Page 74

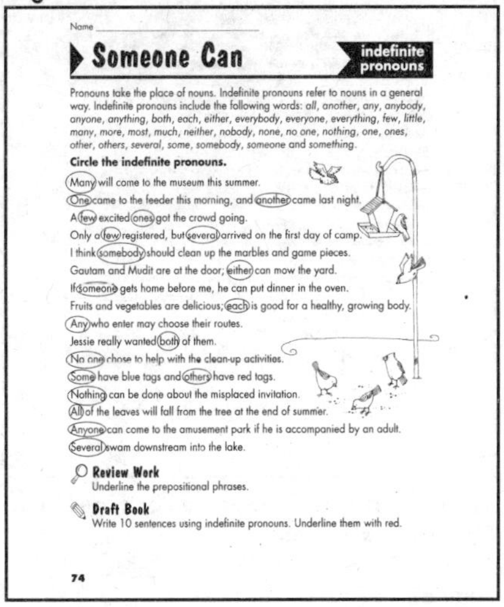

Name ______________

Someone Can — indefinite pronouns

Pronouns take the place of nouns. Indefinite pronouns refer to nouns in a general way. Indefinite pronouns include the following words: all, another, any, anybody, anyone, anything, both, each, either, everybody, everyone, everything, few, little, many, more, most, much, neither, nobody, none, no one, nothing, one, ones, other, others, several, some, somebody, someone and something.

Circle the indefinite pronouns.

(Many) will come to the museum this summer.
(One) came to the feeder this morning, and (another) came last night.
A (few) excited (ones) got the crowd going.
Only a (few) registered, but (several) arrived on the first day of camp.
I think (somebody) should clean up the marbles and game pieces.
Gautam and Mudit are at the door; (either) can mow the yard.
If (someone) gets home before me, he can put dinner in the oven.
Fruits and vegetables are delicious; (each) is good for a healthy, growing body.
(Any) who enter may choose their routes.
Jessie really wanted (both) of them.
(No one) chose to help with the clean-up activities.
(Some) have blue tags and (others) have red tags.
(Nothing) can be done about the misplaced invitation.
(All) of the leaves will fall from the tree at the end of summer.
(Anyone) can come to the amusement park if he is accompanied by an adult.
(Several) swam downstream into the lake.

Review Work Underline the prepositional phrases.

Draft Book Write 10 sentences using indefinite pronouns. Underline them with red.

74

RW: Underline to the museum; to the feeder; on the first day; of camp; at the door; in the oven; for a healthy, growing body; of them; with the clean-up activities; about the misplaced invitation; of the leaves; from the tree; at the end of summer; to the amusement park; by an adult; and into the lake.
DB: Answers will vary.

Page 75

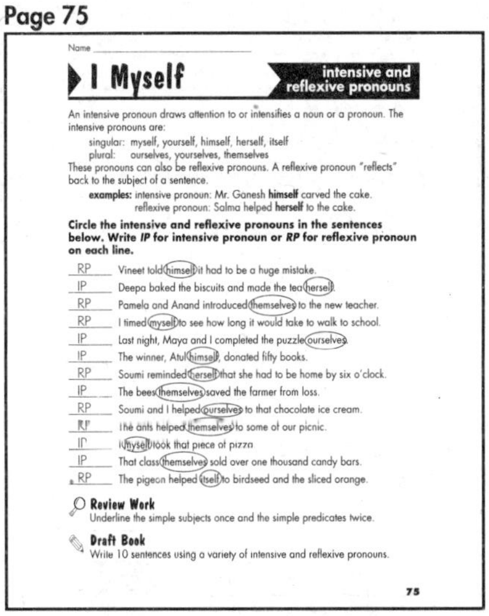

Name ______________

I Myself — intensive and reflexive pronouns

An intensive pronoun draws attention to or intensifies a noun or a pronoun. The intensive pronouns are:
singular: myself, yourself, himself, herself, itself
plural: ourselves, yourselves, themselves
These pronouns can also be reflexive pronouns. A reflexive pronoun "reflects" back to the subject of a sentence.
examples: intensive pronoun: Mr. Ganesh **himself** carved the cake.
reflexive pronoun: Salma helped **herself** to the cake.

Circle the intensive and reflexive pronouns in the sentences below. Write IP for intensive pronoun or RP for reflexive pronoun on each line.

RP — Vineet told (himself) it had to be a huge mistake.
IP — Deepa baked the biscuits and made the tea (herself).
RP — Pamela and Anand introduced (themselves) to the new teacher.
RP — I timed (myself) to see how long it would take to walk to school.
IP — Last night, Maya and I completed the puzzle (ourselves).
IP — The winner, Atul (himself), donated fifty books.
RP — Soumi reminded (herself) that she had to be home by six o'clock.
IP — The bees (themselves) saved the farmer from loss.
RP — Soumi and I helped (ourselves) to that chocolate ice cream.
RP — The ants helped (themselves) to some of our picnic.
IP — I (myself) took that piece of pizza.
IP — That class (themselves) sold over one thousand candy bars.
RP — The pigeon helped (itself) to birdseed and the sliced orange.

Review Work Underline the simple subjects once and the simple predicates twice.

Draft Book Write 10 sentences using a variety of intensive and reflexive pronouns.

75

RW: Underline Vineet, Deepa, Pamela, Anand, I, Maya, I, Atul, Soumi, bees, Soumi, I, ants, I, class and pigen once.
Underline told, barked, introduced, timed, completed, donated, reminded, saved, helped, helped, took, sold and helped twice.
DB: Answers will vary.

Page 76

Name ______________

To or With Whom — interrogative pronouns

Interrogative pronouns are used to ask questions. Sometimes they begin interrogative sentences. The five interrogative pronouns are: what, which, who, whom and whose. Who is used like a subject pronoun; whom is used like an object pronoun. If these words are not being used in place of nouns, they are not interrogative pronouns.

Circle the interrogative pronouns in the sentences below.

I need to know (which) will fit you.
(Which) did you buy, the yellow or green one?
Big Store has (what) you need to finish the tree house.
The teacher knows with (whom) each person is working.
(Whose) are those platters of sandwiches?
(What) are they bringing to the holiday picnic?
The class planned with (whom) each student would read.
Mom wants to know (who) put her finger into the cake's frosting.
(Whose) should we enter in the city competition?
(Who) was talking before?
To (whom) were you speaking on the phone?
With (whom) do you plan to ride home?
We don't know (whose) those are.
Neha knows (which) has won the contest.
Nandita knows (which) will produce the largest blooms.
Sajida doesn't know (who) will take her ticket.
(Which) did Arun choose as his puppy?

Review Work Change one declarative sentence from the top of the page to an interrogative sentence.

Draft Book Write 10 sentences using interrogative pronouns.

76

RW: Answers will vary. DB: Answers will vary.

Page 77

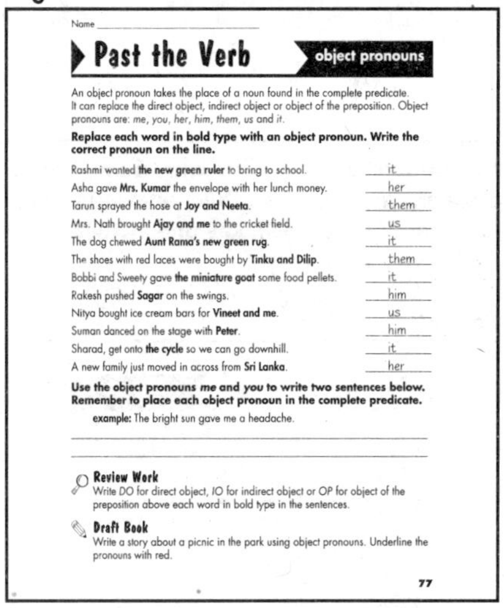

Name ______________

Past the Verb — object pronouns

An object pronoun takes the place of a noun found in the complete predicate. It can replace the direct object, indirect object or object of the preposition. Object pronouns are: me, you, her, him, them, us and it.

Replace each word in bold type with an object pronoun. Write the correct pronoun on the line.

Sentence	Pronoun
Rashmi wanted **the new green ruler** to bring to school.	it
Asha gave **Mrs. Kumar** the envelope with her lunch money.	her
Tarun sprayed the hose at **Joy and Neeta**.	them
Mrs. Nath brought **Ajay and me** to the cricket field.	us
The dog chewed **Aunt Rama's new green rug**.	it
The shoes with red laces were bought by **Tinku and Dilip**.	them
Bobbi and Sweety gave **the miniature goat** some food pellets.	it
Rakesh pushed **Sagar** on the swings.	him
Nitya bought ice cream bars for **Vineet and me**.	us
Suman danced on the stage with **Peter**.	him
Sharad, get onto **the cycle** so we can go downhill.	it
A new family just moved in across from **Sri Lanka**.	her

Use the object pronouns me and you to write two sentences below. Remember to place each object pronoun in the complete predicate.

example: The bright sun gave me a headache.

Review Work Write DO for direct object, IO for indirect object or OP for object of the preposition above each word in bold type in the sentences.

Draft Book Write a story about a picnic in the park using object pronouns. Underline the pronouns with red.

77

Answers will vary. RW: 1. DO 2. IO 3. OP 4. DO 5. DO 6. OP 7. IO 8. DO 9. OP 10. OP 11. OP 12. OP
DB: Answers will vary.

Page 78

Name ______________

It Must Be Mine — possessive pronouns

Possessive pronouns take the place of possessive nouns. They can be used before a noun or after a linking verb. The possessive pronoun its does not have an apostrophe.
before a noun: my, your, his, her, its, our, their
after a linking verb: mine, yours, his, hers, its, ours, theirs
example: My brush is on the table. That brush is **mine**.

Circle each possessive pronoun. Draw an arrow to the noun it modifies.

(Their) mom travels around the state on business.
(Our) house is near the library.
(Its) handle is loose.
The black dog under that bush is (mine).
(Her) socks are in the middle drawer.
We went to the musical with (his) parents.
The house with the pool is (his).
(My) friend asked (my) opinion about which bike to buy.
The salami and cheese sandwich is (hers).
(Their) wooded backyard is a great place to play.
(Her) older cousin is staying at (their) house for a week.
The trophy has (its) own shelf.
(His) old bunk bed was given to (his) younger brother.

Review Work Underline the complete subjects in the sentences. If the possessive noun modifies the simple subject, it is part of the complete subject.

Draft Book Write sentences using the list of possessive pronouns on this page. Use each possessive pronoun at least once.

78

Answer Key

Page 78 (cont.)

RW: Underline their mom, our house, its handle, the black dog under that bush, her socks, we, the house with the pool, my friend, the salami and cheese sandwich, their wooded backyard, her older cousin, the trophy and his old bunk bed. DB: Answers will vary.

Page 79

Name ____________

Throw Some Out — contractions

A contraction is two words that are put together to form one word. An apostrophe replaces the missing letters. Many contractions are formed using pronouns and other words. The following letters are left with the apostrophe when a contraction is made.

'll when adding will (that'll)
'd when adding would or had (we'd)
's when adding is or has (she's)
're when adding are (we're)
've when adding have (I've)

Write the contractions.

I + would = I'd — he + will = he'll
it + is = it's — what + is = what's
they + would = they'd — they + will = they'll

Write the words that form the contractions.

he'd = he would/had — I'll = I will
there've = there have — I'm = I am
we'd = we would/had — she'll = she will

Circle each contraction. Write the words it replaces on the line.

they have — Do you think (they've) gone to the game without us?
they are — Kris and John think (they're) not invited to the party.
she would — Neha said (she'd) bring a blanket to the camp out.
who is — Has Mrs. Dutt decided (who's) making the announcement today?
There is — (There's) enough time to finish the card.
I will — I think (I'll) put the new video on the top shelf.
Here is — (Here's) the key we looked for all morning!

Review Work Underline the nouns with yellow.

Draft Book Write a sentence using each contraction from this page.

79

RW: Underline game, Kris, John, party, Neha, blanket, camp out, Mrs. Dutt, announcement, time, card, video, shelf, key and morning. DB: Answers will vary.

Page 80

Name ____________

Did Not! — contractions: not

A contraction is two words that are put together to form one word. An apostrophe replaces the missing letters. Not is a word that forms contractions with many helping or linking verbs. In contractions, the o in not is replaced with an apostrophe.

example: did + not = didn't

The contraction for will not is an exception: will + not = won't.

Circle each contraction. Write the two words that formed it on the line.

are not — We (aren't) planning to attend the football game tonight.
is not — The plan itself (isn't) to sit around and do nothing.
was not — Renuka (wasn't) in the band room this morning.
should not — Tara (shouldn't) have to do that by herself.
must not — The children (mustn't) put their dirty hands on the sliding door.
can not — That table (can't) take the load of all those bricks.
had not — Jayan (hadn't) done his homework.
would not — Alex (wouldn't) take a snack without asking.
were not — Sara, Gopi and Suma (weren't) at the park yesterday.
has not — The mail carrier (hasn't) driven down Mannadi Street yet.
did not — Mika, our new puppy, (didn't) want to sleep.
have not — Alisha and I (haven't) done our morning chores.
does not — Varun (doesn't) want to eat pizza.
will not — Many (won't) arrive until after the food booth opens.
did not — Omar (didn't) have anyone to help him.
could not — The squirrels (couldn't) get onto the new bird feeder.

Review Work Underline each pronoun with red.

Draft Book Write a sentence using each contraction from this page.

80

RW: Underline we, itself, this, that, herself, their, that, those, his, our, I, our, many, anyone, and him with red. DB: Answers will vary.

Page 81

Name ____________

Combining Sentences — coordinating conjunctions

Sentences can be combined when their ideas are the same. Related sentences can be joined with coordinating conjunctions. There are seven coordinating conjunctions: and, nor, but, for, yet, so and or.

examples: Alex plays tennis. + Alex plays basketball. = Alex plays tennis and basketball.
Anika slept on the plane. + Anika did not sleep on the train. = Anika slept on the plane but not on the train.

Combine each set of sentences using a coordinating conjunction. Write the new sentence on the line.

Devan went swimming in the pool. Devan did not go swimming in the lake.
Devan went swimming in the pool but not in the lake.

The flowers need to be watered. The flowers need to be fertilised.
The flowers need to be watered and fertilised.

Julie remembered her backpack. Julie did not remember her lunch.
Julie remembered her backpack but not her lunch.

We can watch the movie. We can play a game.
We can watch the movie or play a game.

I did not buy candy. I didn't buy chips.
I did not buy candy or chips.

The squirrel jumped on the bird feeder. The squirrel ate the birdseed.
The squirrel jumped on the bird feeder and ate the birdseed.

Latika likes broccoli. Latika likes cauliflower.
Latika likes broccoli and cauliflower.

Review Work Circle the coordinating conjunctions.

Draft Book Write five pairs of sentences that can be combined. Write a combined sentence for each pair.

81

RW: Circle but, and, but, or, or, and, and and. DB: Answers will vary.

Page 82

Name ____________

We Did It — compound subjects

Similar sentences can be combined into one simple sentence with a compound subject by using a coordinating conjunction.

example: Dan studied today. + Jack studied today. = Dan and Jack studied today.
Dan studied today. + Jack did not study today. = Dan but not Jack studied today.

If three or more subjects are combined, use commas to separate them and the conjunction.

example: Dan studied today. + Jack studied today. + Mohit studied today. = Dan, Jack and Mohit studied today.

Underline the compound subject in each sentence.

Blues, minkes and sperm whales are known as great whales.
The biographies but not the anthologies are on the first shelf.
Joe, Micky, Shiela and Hari play trumpets in the band.
Andy and I bought ice-cream sandwiches.
Blue jays, finches, pigeons and mynahs come daily to the bird feeder.

Use a coordinating conjunction to combine each set of sentences into one sentence with a compound subject. Write each sentence on a line.

Jyotika ate salad. Alia ate salad.
Jyotika and Alia ate salad.

Jacob planted the corn. Jeet planted the corn.
Jacob and Jeet planted the corn.

Dolphins are mammals. Whales are mammals. Elephants are mammals.
Dolphins, whales and elephants are mammals.

Review Work In the combined sentences you wrote, underline the complete subjects once and the complete predicates twice.

Draft Book Write five sets of sentences containing first nouns that can be combined. Trade with a partner and combine the sentences.

82

RW: Underline Jyotika and Alia; Jacob and Jeet; and Dolphins, whales and elephants once. Underline ate salad, planted the corn and are mammals twice. DB: Answers will vary.

Page 83

Name ____________

Doing Many Things — combining predicates

Similar sentences can be combined into one simple sentence with a compound predicate by using a coordinating conjunction.

example: Jan planted the seeds. + Jan watered the seeds. = Jan planted and watered the seeds.

Underline the compound predicate in each sentence. Circle each coordinating conjunction.

The rocket ignited (and) blasted off into space.
Balu and Radha washed, vacuumed (and) waxed the car.
The dog broke the leash (and) ran away.
The wind whipped the tree's branches (and) shredded its leaves.
Rajan catches (and) throws during practice.
Mili whipped (and) folded the eggs into the batter.

Use a coordinating conjunction to combine each set of sentences into one sentence with a compound predicate. Write each sentence on a line.

Vipin measured the board. Vipin cut the board.
Vipin measured and cut the board.

Disha swept the floor. Disha mopped the floor. Disha waxed the floor.
Disha swept, mopped and waxed the floor.

The kitten pounced on the ball of yarn. The kitten swatted the ball of yarn.
The kitten pounced on and swatted the ball of yarn.

Punit screamed on the roller coaster. Punit enjoyed the roller coaster.
Punit screamed and/but enjoyed the roller coaster.

Review Work In the combined sentences you wrote, underline the simple subjects once and the simple predicates twice.

Draft Book Write five sets of sentences whose verbs can be combined. Write a combined sentence for each set.

83

Page 83 (cont.)

RW: Underline Vipin, Disha, kitten and Punit once. Underline measured, swept, mopped, waxed, pounced, swatted, screamed and enjoyed twice. DB: Answers will vary.

Page 84

Name ____________

We Can Relate — compound subjects and predicates

Sentences can be combined when their ideas are the same. Related sentences can be joined with coordinating conjunctions.

Circle the coordinating conjunctions. If a sentence has a compound subject write CS. If a sentence has a compound predicate write CP. If it has both, write B.

CS — Salmon (and) walleye swim upstream in that river.
B — Dilip (and) Sara formed (and) threw snowballs.
CS — Bats (and) dragonflies eat mosquitoes.
CP — Trilok bought cotton candy (and) ate it.
B — The grapes (and) apples fell (and) rolled on the floor.
CS — Javed (and) Akhtar growled at the intruder.
B — The horseflies (and) mosquitoes irritated (and) pestered the hikers.
CS — Mercury (and) Venus are between the Sun and Earth.
CP — Joe poured (and) drank the ice water.
CS — The cow (and) its calf live in that pasture.
B — Alok (and) Ekta held (and) watched the sparklers.
CS — Jupiter (and) Saturn have rings.
CP — The machine copied (and) collated the reports.
CS — Lalit (and) Dalia have braces.
B — A tape recorder (but) not a CD player records (and) plays music.
CP — Rohit bit, chewed (and) swallowed the burger.
CP — Jyoti cleaned (and) filleted the fish.

Review Work Write an SS above each simple subject. Underline the simple predicates with blue.

Draft Book Write 10 sentences with compound subjects, compound predicates or both.

84

RW: Write an SS above salmon, walleye, Dilip, Sara, bats, dragonflies, Trilok, grapes, apples, Javed, Akhtar, horseflies, mosquitoes, Mercury, Venus, Joe, cow, calf, Alok, Ekta, Jupiter, Saturn, machine, Lalit, Dalia, tape recorder, player, Rohit and Jyoti. Underline swim, formed, threw, eat, bought, ate, fell, rolled, growled, irritated, pestered, are, poured, drank, live, held, watched, have, copied, collated, have, records, plays, bit, chewed, swallowed, cleaned and filleted with blue. DB: Answers will vary.

Page 85

Name ____________

Can I Stand Alone? — clauses

A clause is a group of words with a subject and a predicate. An independent clause can stand alone as a sentence.

example: Jan plays cricket.

A dependent clause cannot stand alone; it is used with an independent clause.

example: because he likes the sport (not a sentence)
Jan plays cricket because he likes the sport.

Write IC if the group of words is an independent clause. Write DC if the group of words is a dependent clause.

DC — whenever Dilip gets a pickle
IC — everyone teases him
IC — jasmine rides her horse Tally
DC — so Chand bought a new bat
IC — those flowers are blooming early
DC — until Lila decides to finish her homework
IC — i walked a mile before school
DC — since it was thundering and lightning
DC — because the bag of candy was unopened
IC — kishan chewed three sticks of gum
IC — the store closed at six o'clock
DC — if Munir orders french fries
IC — leena hung the picture on the wall
DC — although the power went out
IC — the toilet-paper roll is empty

Review Work Add uppercase letters and punctuation to the sentences above.

Draft Book Write complete sentences using the dependent clauses above.

85

RW: Add uppercase letters and punctuation to sentences. DB: Answers will vary.

Answer Key

Page 86

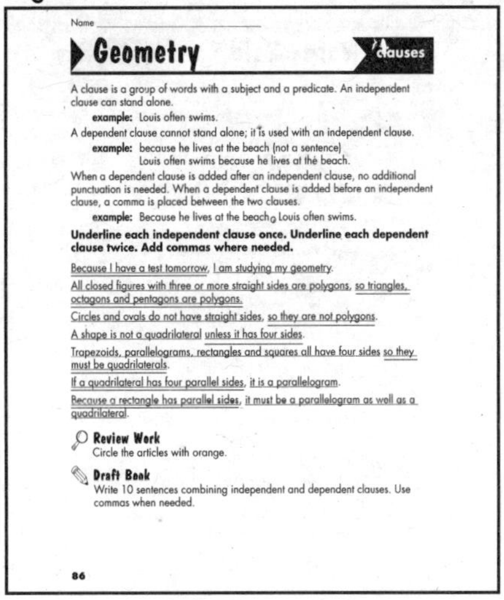

Name

Geometry — clauses

A clause is a group of words with a subject and a predicate. An independent clause can stand alone.
example: Louis often swims.
A dependent clause cannot stand alone; it is used with an independent clause.
example: because he lives at the beach (not a sentence)
Louis often swims because he lives at the beach.
When a dependent clause is added after an independent clause, no additional punctuation is needed. When a dependent clause is added before an independent clause, a comma is placed between the two clauses.
example: Because he lives at the beach, Louis often swims.

Underline each independent clause once. Underline each dependent clause twice. Add commas where needed.

Because I have a test tomorrow, I am studying my geometry.
All closed figures with three or more straight sides are polygons, so triangles, octagons and pentagons are polygons.
Circles and ovals do not have straight sides, so they are not polygons.
A shape is not a quadrilateral unless it has four sides.
Tropezoids, parallelograms, rectangles and squares all have four sides so they must be quadrilaterals.
If a quadrilateral has four parallel sides, it is a parallelogram.
Because a rectangle has parallel sides, it must be a parallelogram as well as a quadrilateral.

Review Work
Circle the articles with orange.

Draft Book
Write 10 sentences combining independent and dependent clauses. Use commas when needed.

86

RW: Circle each a. DB: Answers will vary.

Page 87

Name

Just a Piece — phrases and clauses

A phrase is a group of words that does not have a subject and predicate. A clause is a group of words with a subject and a predicate. An independent clause can stand alone. A dependent clause cannot stand alone.

Write P if the group of words is a phrase. Write IC if the group of words is an independent clause. Write DC if the group of words is a dependent clause.

P with Tom and me
IC Dinesh walks
DC whenever the news comes on television
P running and jumping in the leaves
P around nine o'clock
IC Jaya likes drawing
P is great at editing
DC so that he can get his work done
P shimmering and sparkling in the sun
IC sea turtles swim many miles
P the open bag of potato chips
P little striped fish
DC although I knew the material
P crashing through the woods
DC if Olive wins one more competition
DC after Rahul missed the bus
IC this pen works
IC Firoz mows the lawn

Review Work
Add uppercase letters and punctuation to the independent clauses above.

Draft Book
Use the phrases and dependent clauses to write complete sentences.

87

RW: Add uppercase letters and punctuation to independent clauses. DB: Answers will vary.

Page 88

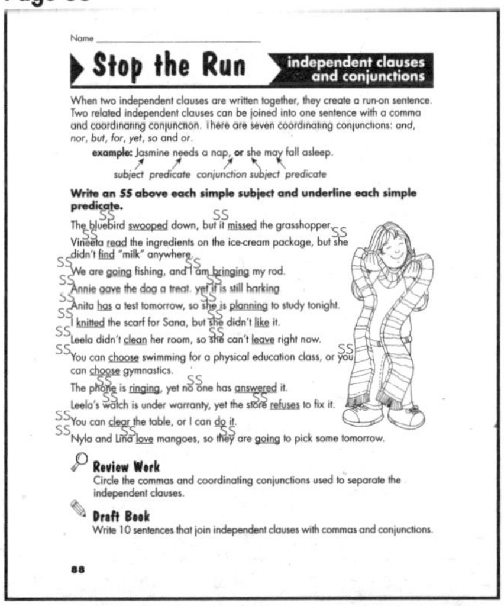

Name

Stop the Run — independent clauses and conjunctions

When two independent clauses are written together, they create a run-on sentence. Two related independent clauses can be joined into one sentence with a comma and coordinating conjunction. There are seven coordinating conjunctions: and, nor, but, for, yet, so and or.
example: Jasmine needs a nap, or she may fall asleep.
subject predicate conjunction subject predicate

Write an SS above each simple subject and underline each simple predicate.

The bluebird swooped down, but it missed the grasshopper.
Vineeta read the ingredients on the ice-cream package, but she didn't find "milk" anywhere.
We are going fishing, and I am bringing my rod.
Annie gave the dog a treat, yet it is still barking.
Anita has a test tomorrow, so she is planning to study tonight.
I knitted the scarf for Sana, but she didn't like it.
Leela didn't clean her room, so she can't leave right now.
You can choose swimming for a physical education class, or you can choose gymnastics.
The phone is ringing, yet no one has answered it.
Leela's watch is under warranty, yet the store refuses to fix it.
You can clear the table, or I can do it.
Nyla and Lina love mangoes, so they are going to pick some tomorrow.

Review Work
Circle the commas and coordinating conjunctions used to separate the independent clauses.

Draft Book
Write 10 sentences that join independent clauses with commas and conjunctions.

88

RW: Circle but, but, and, yet, so, but, so, or, yet, yet, or, so, and the commas that come before them. DB: Answers will vary.

Page 89

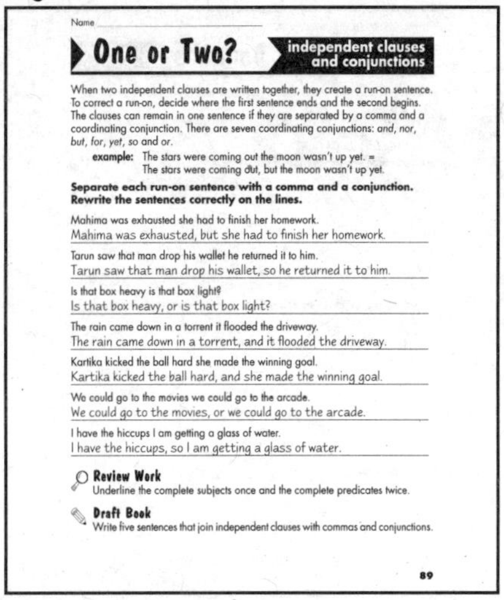

Name

One or Two? — independent clauses and conjunctions

When two independent clauses are written together, they create a run-on sentence. To correct a run-on, decide where the first sentence ends and the second begins. The clauses can remain in one sentence if they are separated by a comma and a coordinating conjunction. There are seven coordinating conjunctions: and, nor, but, for, yet, so and or.
example: The stars were coming out the moon wasn't up yet. = The stars were coming out, but the moon wasn't up yet.

Separate each run-on sentence with a comma and a conjunction. Rewrite the sentences correctly on the lines.

Mahima was exhausted she had to finish her homework.
Mahima was exhausted, but she had to finish her homework.
Tarun saw that man drop his wallet he returned it to him.
Tarun saw that man drop his wallet, so he returned it to him.
Is that box heavy is that box light?
Is that box heavy, or is that box light?
The rain came down in a torrent it flooded the driveway.
The rain came down in a torrent, and it flooded the driveway.
Kartika kicked the ball hard she made the winning goal.
Kartika kicked the ball hard, and she made the winning goal.
We could go to the movies we could go to the arcade.
We could go to the movies, or we could go to the arcade.
I have the hiccups I am getting a glass of water.
I have the hiccups, so I am getting a glass of water.

Review Work
Underline the complete subjects once and the complete predicates twice.

Draft Book
Write five sentences that join independent clauses with commas and conjunctions.

89

RW: Underline Mahima, she, Tarun, he, that box, that box, the rain, it, Kartika, she, we, we, I and I once.
Underline was exhausted, had to finish her homework, saw that man drop his wallet, returned it to him, is heavy, is light, came down in a torrent, flooded the driveway, kicked the ball hard, made the winning goal, could go to the movies, could go to the arcade, have the hiccups and am getting a glass of water twice.
DB: Answers will vary.

Page 90

Name

Move Over a Bit — independent clauses and semicolons

When two independent clauses are written together, they create a run-on sentence. To correct a run-on, decide where the first sentence ends and the second begins. The clauses can be separated into two sentences or remain in one sentence if they are separated by a semicolon.
example: You have a cut bandage it. = You have a cut; bandage it.

Separate each run-on sentence with a semicolon. Rewrite the sentences correctly on the lines.

Walk down the hallway turn right at the end.
Walk down the hallway; turn right at the end.
Please quit crying you are going to be fine.
Please quit crying; you are going to be fine.
Your alarm is ringing turn it off.
Your alarm is ringing; turn it off.
It could rain today take your umbrella with you.
It could rain today; take your umbrella with you.
Pradeep is in my class he sits right next to me.
Pradeep is in my class; he sits right next to me.
The air show is in town we are going today.
The air show is in town; we going today.
Venus is the second planet from the Sun Earth is the third planet.
Venus is the second planet from the Sun; Earth is the third planet.
My nose is cold my cheeks are numb.
My nose is cold; my cheeks are numb.

Review Work
Underline the pronouns with red.

Draft Book
Write five sentences that join independent clauses with semicolons.

90

RW: Underline you, your, it, it, your, you, my, he, me, we, my and my with red.
DB: Answers will vary.

Page 91

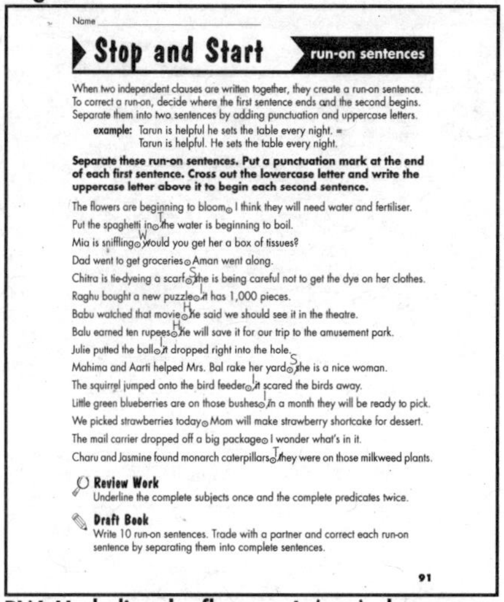

Name

Stop and Start — run-on sentences

When two independent clauses are written together, they create a run-on sentence. To correct a run-on, decide where the first sentence ends and the second begins. Separate them into two sentences by adding punctuation and uppercase letters.
example: Tarun is helpful he sets the table every night. = Tarun is helpful. He sets the table every night.

Separate these run-on sentences. Put a punctuation mark at the end of each first sentence. Cross out the lowercase letter and write the uppercase letter above it to begin each second sentence.

The flowers are beginning to bloom. I think they will need water and fertiliser.
Put the spaghetti in. The water is beginning to boil.
Mia is sniffling. Would you get her a box of tissues?
Dad went to get groceries. Aman went along.
Chitra is tie-dyeing a scarf. She is being careful not to get the dye on her clothes.
Raghu bought a new puzzle. It has 1,000 pieces.
Babu watched that movie. He said we should see it in the theatre.
Balu earned ten rupees. He will save it for our trip to the amusement park.
Julie putted the ball. It dropped right into the hole.
Mahima and Aarti helped Mrs. Bal rake her yard. She is a nice woman.
The squirrel jumped onto the bird feeder. It scared the birds away.
Little green blueberries are on those bushes. In a month they will be ready to pick.
We picked strawberries today. Mom will make strawberry shortcake for dessert.
The mail carrier dropped off a big package. I wonder what's in it.
Charu and Jasmine found monarch caterpillars. They were on those milkweed plants.

Review Work
Underline the complete subjects once and the complete predicates twice.

Draft Book
Write 10 run-on sentences. Trade with a partner and correct each run-on sentence by separating them into complete sentences.

91

RW: Underline the flowers, I, (you), the water, Mia, you, Dad, Aman, Chitra, she, Raghu, it, Babu, he, Balu, he, Julie, it, Mahima and Arti, she, the squirrel, it, little green blueberries, in a month they, we, Mom, the mail carrier, I, Charu and Jasmine, and they once. Underline are beginning to bloom, think they will need water and fertiliser, put the spaghetti in, is beginning to boil, is sniffling, would get her a box of tissues, went to get groceries, went along, is tie-dying a scarf, is being careful not to get the dye on her clothes, bought a new puzzle, has 1,000 pieces, watched that movie, said we should see it in the theatre, earned ten rupees, will save it for our trip to the amusement park, putted the ball, dropped right into the hole, helped Mrs. Bal rake her yard, is a nice woman, jumped onto the bird feeder, scared the birds away, are on those bushes, will be ready to pick, picked strawberries today, will make strawberry shortcake for dessert, dropped off a big package, wonder what's in it, found monarch caterpillars and were on those milkweed plants twice.
DB: Answers will vary.

Page 92

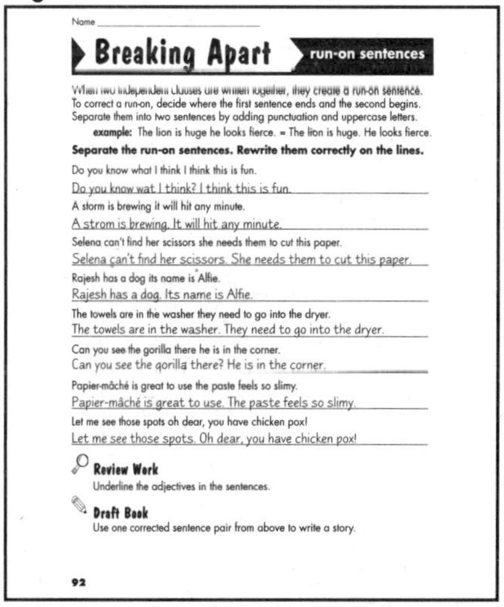

Name

Breaking Apart — run-on sentences

When two independent clauses are written together, they create a run-on sentence. To correct a run-on, decide where the first sentence ends and the second begins. Separate them into two sentences by adding punctuation and uppercase letters.
example: The lion is huge he looks fierce. = The lion is huge. He looks fierce.

Separate the run-on sentences. Rewrite them correctly on the lines.

Do you know what I think I think this is fun.
Do you know wat I think? I think this is fun.
A storm is brewing it will hit any minute.
A strom is brewing. It will hit any minute.
Selena can't find her scissors she needs them to cut this paper.
Selena can't find her scissors. She needs them to cut this paper.
Rajesh has a dog its name is Alfie.
Rajesh has a dog. Its name is Alfie.
The towels are in the washer they need to go into the dryer.
The towels are in the washer. They need to go into the dryer.
Can you see the gorilla there he is in the corner.
Can you see the gorilla there? He is in the corner.
Papier-mâché is great to use the paste feels so slimy.
Papier-mâché is great to use. The paste feels so slimy.
Let me see those spots oh dear, you have chicken pox!
Let me see those spots. Oh dear, you have chicken pox!

Review Work
Underline the adjectives in the sentences.

Draft Book
Use one corrected sentence pair from above to write a story.

92

RW: Underline fun, brewing, any, her, this, great, so slimy, and those.
DB: Answers will vary.

Page 93: Answers will vary.
Page 94: Answers will vary.

Answer Key

Page 95

Name ____________________

Shorten It — abbreviations

Abbreviations of proper nouns, special titles and degrees are capitalised. Abbreviations of most common nouns are not capitalised. When used with a proper adjective, an abbreviation is capitalised. An abbreviation usually ends with a full stop.

examples: J. B. Kinard & Co.
3 Ansari Rd.

Write an abbreviation for each word. Capitalise when needed and add full stops. A few have been done for you.

drive	Dr.	Saturday	Sat.	Senior	Sr.
Mister	Mr.	ounce	oz.	General	Gen.
company	Co.	March	Mar.	street	St.
Private	Pvt.	Saint	St.	yard	yd.
Reverend	Rev.	avenue	Ave.	Sunday	Sun.
Doctor	Dr.	Missus	Mrs.	inch	in.
Monday	Mon.	April	Apr.	et cetera	etc.
December	Dec.	Thursday	Thurs.	feet	ft.
Post Office	P.O.	January	Jan.	February	Feb.
Friday	Fri.	August	Aug.	September	Sept.
October	Oct.	pound	lb.	Junior	Jr.
Wednesday	Wed.	dozen	doz.	November	Nov.
incorporated	Inc.	Tuesday	Tues.	boulevard	Blvd.
United States	U.S.				

Review Work
Draw an X next to each proper noun.

Draft Book
Begin a list of abbreviations for future reference. Write each full word and its abbreviation.

95

RW: Draw an X next to Monday, December, Friday, October, Wednesday, United States, Saturday, March, April, Thursday, January, August, Tuesday, Sunday, February, September and November. DB: Answers will vary.

Page 96

Name ____________________

Hey! — interjections

Interjections show strong feelings or sudden emotions. They can be words or just sounds, gasps, or exclamations that are more like noises than regular words. An interjection usually comes at the beginning of a sentence, often an exclamatory sentence. It can be followed by an exclamation mark or a comma.

Common interjections: aha, ahem, goodness, gracious, gross, grr, hello, help, hey, hooray, no, nonsense, oh, oops, ouch, phew, psst, rats, shh, super, terrific, thanks, ugh, well, wow, yes, yikes, yuck

Draw a box around each interjection and the punctuation following it.

[OK,] I understand this now.
[Shh!] We're trying to get our work done.
[Ouch,] get off my foot!
[Wow!] I passed!
[Mmmm,] something smells delicious!
[Really,] would you do that for me?
[Stop!] That isn't very nice.
[Hold on,] I'm almost finished.
[Oops!] I broke the lead on another pencil.
[Hey,] give that back!

Review Work
Write an SS above the simple subject in each sentence. Underline the simple predicates with blue.

Draft Book
Write 10 sentences using interjections. Write some that need commas and some that need exclamation marks.

96

RW: Write an SS above I, we, (you), I, something, you, that, I, I, and (you). DB: Answers will vary.

Page 97

Name ____________________

Here and There — commas

Proper nouns name special people, places and things. When proper nouns name a city and state, a comma goes between them.

example: Madurai, Tamil Nadu

Write the addresses correctly. Apply what you know about abbreviations. Capitalise all proper nouns. Put a comma between each city and state name.

mrs seem ray — Mrs. Seema Ray
4268/3 andheri east — 4268/3 Andheri East
mumbai maharashtra 400099 — Mumbai, Maharashtra 400 099

dr suresh r nagarajan — Dr. Suresh R. Nagarajan
12 masilamani street — 12 Masilamani Street
chennai tamil nadu 600017 — Chennai, Tamil Nadu 600 017

Add uppercase letters and commas where needed.

Mrs. Naidu's granddaughter lives in Hyderabad, Andhra Pradesh.
Sai got a package from Bhopal, Madhya Pradesh.
Monika ordered some clothing from Mumbai, Maharashtra.
Rahim sent a letter from Surat, Gujarat to Patiala, Punjab.
Pradeep stayed overnight in Madurai, Tamil Nadu.

Review Work
Circle the neuter nouns in the sentences above.

Draft Book
Create an address page. Write the addresses of your friends, classmates, teachers, etc. Use commas, uppercase letters and abbreviations correctly.

97

RW: Circle package, clothing, letter, and Town. DB: Answers will vary.

Page 98

Name ____________________

Put in Your Commas — commas in dates

Commas are used in certain dates to separate the day of the week, the month and date, and the year.

yes: Saturday, March 15 — no: March 15
yes: Saturday, March 15, 2003 — no: March 2003
yes: March 15, 2003

Add commas where needed in the dates.

Sunday August 18 1991 — Sunday, August 18, 1991
Wednesday February 26 — Wednesday, February 26
October 11 1973 — October 11, 1973
December 30 — December 30
Tuesday June 29 — Tuesday, June 29
May 2003 — May 2003
July 4 1880 — July 4, 1880

Rewrite each sentence correctly. Write out abbreviated words.

The first practice is Sat. Sept. 3.
The first practice is Saturday, September 3.
Samuel's birthday is Feb. 15.
Samuel's birthday is February 15.
Sasha was born Tues. Jan. 30 2001.
Sasha was born Tuesday, Jan 30, 2001.
Trishita will graduate Thurs. June 11.
Trishita will graduate Thursday, June 11.

Review Work
Choose two dates from the first section of the page. Rewrite them using abbreviations.

Draft Book
Write 10 sentences using dates. Add commas as needed.

98

RW: Write two of the following: Sun., Aug. 18, 1991; Wed., Feb. 26; Oct. 11, 1973; Dec. 30; and Tues., June 29. DB: Answers will vary.

Page 99

Name ____________________

Reading and Viewing — titles

Underline the titles of books, magazines, newspapers, plays, movies, musicals and television shows. In typed form, these titles are often italicised instead of underlined. Quotation marks go around subsets of the above: article titles, chapter titles, essays, short stories, songs and poems. Capitalise the first and last words of a title, as well as any important words (not a preposition or article unless it is the first or last word).

Correct the titles.

Book:
walking through the waves — Walking through the Waves
Magazine or Newspaper:
the times of india — The Times of India
Movie:
monsoon wedding — Monsoon Wedding
Play, Musical or Opera:
bombay dreams — Bombay Dreams
Television Show:
mastermind india — Mastermind India

Underline the titles in the sentences.

We watch Mastermind India every Saturday night.
Raja and I went to the theatre to see Harry Potter.
Madame Butterfly is my mother's favourite opera.
Can Susie read The Hindu when you are done with it?
Kapil is in a play called Now We Are Great.

Review Work
Circle the articles with orange.

Draft Book
Look through several pages of writing in your Draft Book and check your use of titles. Make corrections where necessary.

99

RW: Circle a, the, the, and a with orange. DB: Answers will vary.

Page 100

Name ____________________

Now Read This — quotation marks

Underline the titles of books, magazines, newspapers, plays, movies, musicals and television shows. In typed form, these titles are often italicised instead of underlined. Quotation marks go around subsets of the above: article titles, chapter titles, essays, short stories, songs and poems. Capitalise the first and last words of a title, as well as any important words (not a preposition or article unless it is the first or last word).

Correct the titles.

Chapter Title:
the broken arm — "The Broken Arm"
Essay or Short Story:
how to complete your homework — "How to Complete Your Homework"
Song:
blowing in the wind — "Blowing in the Wind"
Poem:
no means no — "No Means No"

Put quotation marks around the titles.

Mary memorised the poem "The Tower" for her presentation.
Harish handed in his essay "How to Handle Little Sisters".
Since he just finished "Evening in September," Nikhil now has only two chapters left.
This article called "Of Course My Dog Ate It" is funny.
Can Jessie read "New Park Opens" when you are done with the paper?
If you whistle "Summer Song," the dog will howl with you.

Review Work
Circle the indefinite nouns in the sentences above.

Draft Book
Look through several pages of writing in your Draft Book and check your use of quotation marks. Make corrections where necessary.

100

RW: Circle dog and dog. DB: Answers will vary.

Page 101

Name ____________________

The Words Said — quotations

Direct quotations are treated in a special way. The first word of a direct quotation is capitalised. Quotation marks go around the words people say. Punctuation at the end or at a break in the quote goes inside the quotation marks.

examples: Ravi said, "This is fun."
"Stop that!" exclaimed Ravi.
"I did not hear you. What did you say?" asked Ravi.
"I like this," said Ravi.

Rewrite each sentence correctly on the line. Add quotation marks, other punctuation and uppercase letters as needed.

shekhar declared this state is a great place
Shekhar declared, "This state is a great place!"
hand washing prevents the spread of germs explained dr chandra
"Hand washing prevents the spread of germs," explained Dr. Chandra.
I am smarter than you retorted hari
"I am smarter than you," retorted Hari.
can i have a peanut asked jesse
"Can I have a peanut?" asked Jesse.
can't you ever quit annoying me sighed jamal
"Can't you ever quit annoying me?" sighed Jamal.
she exclaimed my red pen has run out of ink
She exclaimed, "My red pen has run out of ink."
would you like to have pizza questioned aryan
"Would you like to have pizza?" questioned Aryan.

Review Work
Draw an X next to each proper noun that names a person.

Draft Book
Write a sentence for each verb used instead of *said*. Put quotation marks around the words people or characters say.

101

RW: Draw an X next to Shekhar, Dr. Chandra, Hari, Jesse, Jamal and Aryan. DB: Answers will vary.

Page 102

Name ____________________

You Just Keep Talking — quotations

Direct quotations are treated in a special way. The first word of a direct quotation is capitalised. Quotation marks go around the words people say. Punctuation at the end or at a break in the quote goes inside the quotation marks.

examples: "Since you have prepaid tickets," stated the desk clerk, "you may enter to the right."
"This is awful," sighed Bobby. "Everything we typed was just lost."

Rewrite each sentence correctly on the line. Add quotation marks, other punctuation and uppercase letters as needed.

i really think malti insisted there is a better way
"I really think," Malti insisted, "there is a better way."
put your books away stated ms ray the test begins now
"Put your books away," stated Mr. Ray, "the test begins now."
the mail capt a c hari announced has arrived
"The Mail," Capt. A. C. Hari announced, "has arrived."
can't you leave me alone lucy grunted i'm busy
"Can't you leave me alone?" Lucy grunted. "I'm busy."
you said we could go soon persisted beena can we go now
"You said we could go soon," persisted Beena. "Can we go now?"
i wonder questioned leela why the cat won't eat the watermelon
"I wonder," questioned Leela, "why the cat won't eat the watermelon."
i will be on the patio explained amy reading my new book
"I will be on the patio," explained Amy, "reading my new book."

Review Work
Draw an X next to each proper noun that names a person.

Draft Book
Begin a list of alternate words for said. Refer to this list for future writing assignments.

102

RW: Draw an X next to Malti, Ms. Ray, Capt. A.C.Hari, Lucy, Beena, Leela and Amy. DB: Answers will vary.

Page 103

Name ____________________

One Inside the Other — single quotation marks

When a word is highlighted or a title is used inside a direct quote, single quotation marks are used.

example: Sheila said, "I can't seem to spell the word 'peninsula' correctly in this paper."

At the end of a quote, the ending punctuation comes between the single and double quotation marks.

example: "Why can't I spell 'peninsula'?" asked Sheila.

Rewrite each sentence correctly. Add quotation marks, single quotation marks, other punctuation and uppercase letters as needed.

rupa said i read the article bike safety by mike b helmet
Rupa said, "I read the article 'Bike Safety' by Mike B. Helmet."
would you play fur elise on the piano asked gowri
"Would you play 'Fur Elise' on the piano?" asked Gowri.
my essay life in antarctica is due tomorrow explained ramu
"My essay 'Life in Antarctica' is due tomorrow," explained Ramu.
how do you spell kangaroo questioned meera
"How do you spell 'kangaroo'?" questioned Meera.
we have to read nighttime maya complained it is the longest chapter
"We have to read 'Nighttime,'" Maya complained. "It is the largest Chapter."
mom said you certainly may when i asked her replied jay
"Mom said, 'You certainly may' when I asked her," replied Jay.
mr amir announced we are going to sing vande mataram
Mr. Amir announced, "We are going to sing 'Vande Mataram'."

Review Work
Draw an X next to each proper noun that names a person. Draw a triangle next to each proper noun that names a place.

Draft Book
Add to your list of alternate words for said.

103

RW: Draw an X next to Rupa, Mike B. Helmet, Gowri, Ramu, Meera, Maya, Mom, Jay and Mr. Amir.Draw a triange above Antarctica. DB: Answers will vary.